THE FALCON
UNDER THE HAT
Russian Merry Tales
and Fairy Tales

THE FALCON UNDER THE HAT

RUSSIAN MERRY TALES AND FAIRY TALES

Selected and Translated
by Guy Daniels

Illustrated by Feodor Rojankovsky

FUNK & WAGNALLS, NEW YORK

om *Ivan the Merchant's Son and Vasilisa the Wise*

TEXT COPYRIGHT © 1969 BY GUY DANIELS
ILLUSTRATIONS COPYRIGHT © 1969 BY FEODOR ROJANKOVSKY
FIRST PUBLISHED, 1969, BY FUNK & WAGNALLS,
A DIVISION OF READER'S DIGEST BOOKS, INC.
LIBRARY OF CONGRESS CATALOGUE CARD NUMBER: 68-26418
PRINTED IN THE UNITED STATES OF AMERICA
1

FOREWORD

I

OVER MANY CENTURIES, in Russia, religious literature was the only kind deemed worthy of being written down for posterity. All other kinds were preserved merely by word of mouth. It was not until the 17th century that poetry and "polite" fiction began to be printed. And it was not until two centuries later that the Russians actually began to record on paper some of their vast hoard of folklore.*

Thus for a long time after the folk and fairy tales of other European countries had been written down and were being *read*, the Russian tales continued, always and only, to be *told* and *heard*. (One might even say they were performed, like playlets or vaudeville skits, with each skillful teller contributing his own flourishes and embellishments as the story went through countless retell-

---

* The first—and for almost two centuries, the only—collection of Russian folk tales was made by an Englishman, Dr. Samuel Collins, who served as court physician to Tsar Aleksei Mikhailovich in the 1660's. His modest sheaf of Russian tales was published in London in 1671.

ings.) Nor has the art of *viva voce* storytelling yet completely died out in Russia, although the trained teller of Russian tales, like the Irish shanachie, is rapidly (and unfortunately) becoming a rarity.

It is this word-of-mouth tradition that accounts, more than anything else perhaps, for the differences between the Russian tales and those more familiar to us. On the one hand, it accounts for the loose structure and meandering in such fairy tales as "Ivan the Merchant's Son." Or the lapses in "The Magic Ring," wherein Zhurka the dog and Vaska the cat are introduced to the reader and then forgotten completely until they are needed again to help Martin out of his predicament. This kind of sloppiness is seldom if ever found in the stories of a literary artist like Hans Christian Andersen. But the tellers of these tales were not literary artists: they were, and are, much more like the "stand-up" comics of our day, excellent not in literary compositions of large design but in miniatures. Hence the perfection of the short "merry tales," with their rapid-fire dialogue (sharpened, as in a vaudeville skit, by many a retelling), and their insets of humorous verse within the prose context of the narrative. One example of such embellishment is the patter introducing "The Crane and the Heron." Another is the ludicrous rhymes in "The Falcon Under the Hat": "He made a kow-tow / a low, humble bow / to the sow." And there are many, many others, including the famous formula for ending a story: "I was there, and I drank beer, but it ran down my mustache and didn't get into my mouth." By which, of course, the storyteller means he's thirsty now, so will his listeners please give him a glass of something.

Another result of the oral tradition is the existence of a bewildering number of different versions of one and the same basic story. There are, of course, many variants of almost all well-known folk tales—even those which have long been fixed in writing. For instance, in "Little Red Riding Hood," as it was first told by Charles Perrault in the 17th century, the little girl was eaten by the wolf. But this seemed too cruel to some of the translators of Perrault's story, so they changed things around, and had Little Red Riding Hood saved by the woodcutters. Aristotle said that storytellers always want to improve on the story they are telling. And if this is true of those who rewrite stories (or poems, like Robert Lowell), it is even more true of those who retell them aloud—especially, it would seem, of the Russians, who have elaborated hundreds of different versions.

Now, in putting together a collection of folk tales, the question always arises: Should I simply choose the one version of each story that I like best? Or should I take the best parts of all the different versions and combine them into a new whole? My own decision, for this collection, was to choose my favorite version—leaving myself free, however, to borrow a detail here and there. Thus in "The Fox and the Wolf" I took the basic story from one source and the verse at the end from another. And in "The Shrewish Wife" I exercised my prerogative as a storyteller and added a detail or two from personal experience—the green raspberries, for one thing.

II

The Russian tellers of tales, as I have remarked, excel in their recitation of the short "merry tale," as opposed to the "fairy" tale.* (Indeed, there are about twice as many merry tales as fairy tales in Russian folklore, and this proportion has been preserved in the present collection.) The differences between the two types

---

* *The Russians have no special designation for what we mean (or so I take it) in English by "fairy tale": a story involving* faërie, *or enchantment, serious in intent, which most often has a happy ending.*

are many and interesting. Most interesting of all, it seems to me, is the one I would like to touch on by way of concluding this introductory note: the difference in the treatment of female characters.

In the merry tales, the woman is for the most part stupid, in contrast to the American family comedies on television and radio wherein the wife is the smart one and the husband and father, nine times out of ten, is a likable simpleton. But the Russian fairy tales are something else again. In this realm of enchantment and seriousness, it is the woman who has the brains—and the magic power, to boot—be she a princess or the old witch, Baba-Yaga. The so-called hero is usually nothing more than a decent chap who has the good sense to do what the woman tells him to do. Also, in many of these tales, he is kind to animals who later on help him out of a bad scrape—and in so doing show themselves to be far more clever than he. Sometimes, it is true, he does perform heroic feats; but even then it is usually upon instructions from the woman, who aids him with her magic and her superior brains. In the Russian *byliny*, or folk epics, the hero performs great feats all on his own. But in the Russian fairy tale, it is the *woman* who is both puissant and wise.

One might easily make a joke of this, and say that fairy tales are by definition stories of wishful thinking: wouldn't it be wonderful if women really *were* strong and wise? But fairy tales, we must remember, are basically serious. Nor, in Russian literature, is the cult of female strength and intelligence confined to their province. That cult is to be found almost everywhere in the works of the greatest Russian writers, be the women good or evil: in the novels of Turgenev, Dostoevski, and Tolstoy; and, in our day, in the poetry of Yevtushenko and Voznesensky.

This exaltation of woman (in the serious stories, not the comic ones) is only one of the many strong bonds between the Russians' folklore and their highest achievements in literary art. And all these common bonds are reminders of an old truth almost completely forgotten in our time, namely, that fairy tales are not just for children. The adult who believes that they are is the fondest believer of all.

Guy Daniels

CONTENTS

TO MATTHEW,
AGAIN

HERE WAS an old peasant woman who had two sons. One of them died, and the other soon after went off on a long trip. A few days after he had left, a soldier on furlough passed through the village and stopped at the old lady's door.

"Grandma," said he, "can you give me a place to sleep tonight?"

"To be sure," said she. "Come right on in. What is your name and where are you from?"

"I'm the Soldier Semyón from the Great Beyond."

"Ah!" the old lady cried. "My darling son died just a short time ago. Did you see him Up There where you come from?"

"I most surely did. We were bunkmates, Grandma."

"Well, I never! What does he do there, pray tell?"

"He herds birds."

"He what?"

"He herds birds, Grandma—and cranes in particular."

"Ach! That sounds like hard work. The poor lad must get very tired."

15

"It's hard work, all right. The cranes, you see, are always getting into the brier patches."

"You don't say! Then the poor lad's clothing must be nearly in shreds!"

"Oh, yes! He's in nothing but rags and tatters."

"My poor boy! I'll tell you what, Semyón. I've got forty yards of cloth here in the house. Would you be so kind as to take it up to my son?"

"Gladly."

"And while you're at it, you might take him some money. I'll give you ten rubles—all I have left."

"I'll make sure that he gets it, Grandma."

The next morning the soldier went happily on his way. Some time after that—maybe a long time, maybe a short one—the old woman's other son, Fedka by name, came home.

"Well, and how didst thou fare while I was away, Mother mine?" he asked.

"I had a visitor," said she proudly. "It was Soldier Semyón from the Great Beyond. He told me all about my dear son, thy brother. They were bunkmates Up There. So I gave him some cloth and ten rubles to take back to my boy."

"Thou didst? Then, Mother mine, I'll be saying good-by. I'll go, now, and wander through the wide world. If I find any greater fool than thyself, I'll come back and take care of thee for the rest of thy life. If I find no such fool, thou canst fend for thyself!" Then he turned on his heel and set off.

When he had wandered a ways, he came to a big manor house and stopped by the barnyard. There he saw an old sow with her little pigs all around her. Fedka got down on his knees and made a kow-tow—a low, humble bow—to the sow.

The *barinya*, or lady of the manor house, saw him from a win-

16

dow, and said to her maid, "Go on out there and ask that peasant what makes him bow to a sow."

The maid ran out and asked Fedka, "Peasant, my mistress would like to know why you kow-tow to a sow?"

"You can tell your mistress for me," he replied, "that her spotted sow is my sister-in-law-to-be. We're getting married to-morrow, the sow's sister and me, and I came to ask her to the wedding. I'd like her to be the bridesmaid—with your mistress' permission. Also, could she please let the piglets come to join in the wedding procession?"

When her maid told her this, the lady said, "What a fool! Imagine asking a sow to a wedding—and the baby pigs, too! Well, it's time all you servants had some amusement, so here's what we'll do. Put my fine fur coat on the sow and have two horses hitched to the carriage. It wouldn't be proper for them to walk to the marriage."

The coach was brought up, and the sow, in the lady's fine coat, together with all her piglets, was put inside. Then Fedka climbed up on the coachman's seat, and off he went.

When the *barin*, the lord of the manor house, came home from his hunting, he was met by his lady, laughing as though she would burst. "I'm *so* glad you're back, my dear!" said she. "Now I have someone to laugh with me! A peasant came by and made a kow-tow to our sow. 'Your spotted sow,' said he, 'is my sister-in-law-to-be.' He asked her to come to the wedding and act as brides-maid. And he asked the piglets to come and hold up the bride's train."

"And of course you gave him the sow."

"Yes, I let her go off with him, my dear. I put my fur coat on her, and lent them a coach and pair."

"Where is the peasant from?"

"Why, I don't know, dovey. Why should I?"

"Because it turns out that it's not the peasant who is a fool—it's you!"

The barin was furious that his wife had been tricked. He rushed out of the house, jumped on a fast horse, and went off in pursuit of Fedka.

Fedka heard him coming. Quickly he drove the coach into the thick woods. Then he came back, sat down at the roadside, took off his hat, and set it on the ground beside him, brim-side down.

"I say there, you with the beard!" the barin cried. "Have you by any chance seen a peasant driving a coach with a sow and her little pigs inside?"

"How could I forget such a sight?" Fedka replied. "He went past a long time ago."

"Which way? How can I catch up with him?"

"Why, just keep going, and don't give in. But there's many a side road—lots and lots. The first thing you know, you'll find you're lost."

"Then come along, fellow, and show me the way. Catch that peasant for me. Could you do that?"

"Oh, no, I couldn't, I'm sorry to say. You see, I've got a falcon here under my hat."

"I'll stay here and guard him for you."

"All right. But be careful and don't let him get away. He's a valuable bird. If he got loose, and my master found out, there'd be the devil to pay!"

"How much is he worth?"

"Oh, three hundred rubles, more or less."

"Well, if he gets away, I'll pay. All right?"

"Not quite. You're making a promise now. But how do I know that you'll stick to it—how?"

"Fie! You don't trust any man—I can see from your face. Well, here's three hundred rubles, just in case."

So Fedka took the money, got on the fast horse, and went galloping off through the woods, while the barin stayed there guarding the hat with nothing under it.

He stayed there a long time. Finally the sun began to set, and the bearded peasant was not back yet.

The barin said to himself, "I'll just take a quick look. It's probably no falcon—only a rook."

So he very cautiously lifted the brim. But you and I know what he saw beneath: nothing at all.

"Something fishy here!" he growled. "Something shady! I'll bet that's the same rogue who cozened my lady!" Then he spat in disgust at himself and at life, and went crawling back home to face up to his wife.

But Fedka, for his part, was already home. To his mother he said, "Mother mine, have no fears; thou canst live here with me. Thou art a fool, but this world has other fools bigger than thou. And two of those fools, just now, gave me—absolutely free—three hundred rubles, a coach and three horses, plus a litter of pigs and the sow."

THE CRANE AND THE HERON

N Owl went winging through the air —a She-Owl she was, and a silly thing. She flew to a tree, and there she sat; she wiggled her tail and looked this way and that; and then once again she took wing. She flew to a tree, and there she sat; she wiggled her tail, and looked this way and that. . . . This is only a flourish—a *tum-tee-tum*; the story itself is yet to come.

A Crane and a Heron lived in a swamp; each one had built himself a little hut at the opposite end of the swamp from the other. The Crane became bored with living alone and decided he would get married. "I think I'll go and propose to the Heron," he said to himself.

So off he flew—flap, flap. He flew for five miles across the swamp and came to the Heron's hut.

"Is Miss Heron at home?"

"I am she."

"Will you marry me?"

"No, Mr. Crane, I will not. Your legs are too long, and your coat is too short. Besides that, your flying is poor. And you couldn't support me, I'm sure. So be off with you, Spindleshanks!"

Back home went the Crane, having got nothing for his pains.

But later on the Heron had second thoughts. "I'd be better off marrying the Crane," she said to herself, "than living here all alone."

So she went to see the Crane. "Mr. Crane," said she, "take me to wife."

"No, Miss Heron, I have no need of you. I don't want to get married. I won't marry you. Go away!"

The Heron shed tears of mortification and went back home.

The Crane began thinking things over again and said to himself, "It was stupid of me not to take Miss Heron to wife. After all, I'm tired of living alone. I'll go right this minute and marry her!"

So he went to see her and said, "Miss Heron, I've decided to marry you. Will you be my wife?"

"No, Mr. Crane, I will not be your wife."

Back home again went the Crane. Then the Heron once more changed her mind. "Why did I turn him down?" she thought. "Why should I live alone? I'd do better to marry the Crane."

So she came to him and proposed, but the Crane was not so disposed.

And to this very day they keep going back and forth, proposing to each other. But they'll never get married!

BLABBERMOUTH

HERE WAS once an old man whose wife was a terrible blabbermouth. She couldn't keep a thing to herself. If you told her something one minute, the next minute the whole town would know about it.

One day when he was out in the woods checking his traps, the old man found a buried treasure. When he had dug it up, he said to himself, "What shall I do with this treasure? If I take it home now, my old woman will tell everybody about it. And when the barin finds out, he'll claim it as his own, because it was found on his land. I'll have to think of something."

So he buried the treasure again, marked the place, and started for home, thinking and thinking.

On the way back, he checked his fishnet and found a pike in it. He took the pike out, dropped the net back in the river, and went on.

Next he checked his rabbit trap and saw he had caught a rabbit. He took the rabbit out and put the pike in its place. Then he took the rabbit back to the river and put it in the fishnet.

When he got home that evening, he told his wife, "Old Woman, light up the stove and bake us some pancakes."

"What are you saying? Whoever bakes pancakes at night?"

24

"Never mind. Just do what I tell you."

So the old woman made a fire in the stove and started baking pancakes and serving them to her husband. He would eat one and then, while her back was turned, put two or three into his knapsack. She kept on baking and the pancakes kept on disappearing. Finally she asked him, "Why are you eating so many? You'll eat us out of house and home!"

"I'll tell you why," he said. "Today I found a buried treasure in the woods. We have to go there tonight and bring it home. It's a long walk, so we'll need plenty of food in our stomachs."

The old woman was so overjoyed she could hardly eat her own plateful of pancakes.

They set out to get the treasure. The old man walked well ahead of his wife, and every now and then he would take a pancake out of his knapsack and hang it on the branch of a tree.

As soon as the old woman saw one of the hanging pancakes, she called, "Come back here! Come back and see what I've found! A pancake hanging from a tree!"

The old man came back and looked. "What's so odd about that? Didn't you notice that pancake cloud moving ahead of us, just touching the treetops?"

"No," said she, "I didn't. Most of the time I was looking down at the ground, so I wouldn't stumble in the dark."

They walked on a good long way, and then the old man said, "Let's go over here and take a look at the rabbit trap I set this morning." When they got to the trap, he reached down and took out the pike.

"Well, I never!" exclaimed the old woman. "How do you suppose that fish ever got into your rabbit trap?"

"What's so odd about that? Didn't you know that some fish walk on the ground?"

"Never in my life did I hear of such a thing! I would never have

believed it, except that I've seen it now with my own two eyes."

They came to the river, and the old woman said, "Your fishnets are somewhere hereabouts. Let's take a look at them."

The old man pulled up a net, and there was a rabbit!

"Well, bless my soul!" exclaimed the old woman. "What strange goings-on tonight! Imagine a rabbit caught in a fishnet!"

"What's so odd about that? You mean to say you never saw a water rabbit?"

"Never once in my life!"

"Well, you've seen one now."

Soon they came to the place where the treasure was buried. The old man dug it up, put the money in his knapsack, and they started for home.

As they were going past the barin's sheep farm, they heard a loud "Meh-eh-eh-eh! Meh-eh-eh!"

The old woman was scared half out of her wits. "What's that?" she cried. "That horrible yelling and wailing?"

"That's the barin. The Devil is beating him. Come on! Let's run! We don't want the Devil to catch us, too!"

So they ran home and got there all out of breath. When they had rested a bit, the old man took the treasure and hid it under the floor of the hut. "Now remember, Old Wife," he said, "you mustn't tell a soul that we have all this money."

"Of course not! What makes you think I'd do that?"

Late the next morning, the old woman took her bucket and went to the village well for some water. "Good morning, Tatiana," a neighbor woman greeted her. "Why have you come so late?"

"Oh, we were up most of the night. You see, my man found a buried treasure. We had to go to the woods last night to dig it up. You never saw so much money in all your life!"

That same day the whole village heard about the treasure. The barin heard about it, too, and sent for the old man.

"Why didn't you tell me you had found a treasure?" he demanded.

"A treasure? I don't know anything about any treasure."

"Don't you try to conceal things from me!" the barin shouted at him. "I know all about it, anyway. Your wife has told everybody."

"But my old woman is not quite right in the head. She tells things that never happened and never will."

"Well, we'll see about that!" And the barin sent for the old woman.

When she got there, he asked, "Did your husband find a buried treasure?"

"Yes, sir, he did."

"And did you go with him to dig it up?"

"Yes, sir, I did."

"Tell me everything that happened."

"Well, first we went through the woods where the pancakes were hanging from the trees."

"*What?* What pancakes?"

"Why, the pancakes from the pancake cloud, silly! Then we came to the rabbit trap and took out a fish. Next we came to the fishnet and took out a rabbit. Then we got to where the treasure was and dug it up. On our way back home, we went past your farm, sir, just when the Devil was beating you."

"*What's that?* What are you saying, you old idiot?" The barin was furious and all red in the face.

"You see?" said the old man. "My old woman says things that just can't be believed."

"Yes, I see, all right!" said the barin, still red in the face. "Run along home, both of you, and don't bother me ever again."

So the old man went happily home with his wife. And to this day, whenever he thinks of the barin, he laughs to himself.

THE SNAKE*

HERE WAS a certain woman who had a daughter by the name of Masha. One day Masha and her girl friends went for a swim. The girls took off their smocks, laid them down on the bank, and jumped into the water.

Out of the water a big snake came crawling. He coiled himself up on Masha's smock. A little while later the other girls came out, put on their clothes, and hurried home. When Masha went to get her smock and saw the big snake lying on it, she picked up a stick and was about to drive him off. But the snake lifted up his head and began to talk to her in a croaking kind of human voice.

"Masha, Masha! Promise you will marry me," he said.

Masha began to cry. "Give me back my smock," she said, "and I will do anything."

"Will you marry me?"

"Yes, I will," Masha said.

The snake crawled off the smock and went back into the water.

Masha dressed and ran home. When she got there, she said to her mother: "Mama, a snake was lying on my smock. And he told

* *A fairy tale by Leo N. Tolstoy.*

me, 'Marry me, or I won't give you back your smock.' So I promised I would."

Her mother just laughed and said, "That was something you dreamed."

A week later a whole army of snakes crawled up to Masha's house.

When Masha saw them she became frightened. "Mama," she said, "the snakes have come after me."

Her mother did not believe her. But when she saw the snakes, she herself became frightened. She locked the gate at the end of the passageway and she locked the door of the hut. The snakes crawled under the gate and along the passageway, but they couldn't get into the hut. So they crawled back again, rolled themselves up into one big ball, and threw themselves at the window. They broke the window and fell through onto the floor of the hut. They crawled along the benches and the tables and up onto the stove, where Masha was hiding in a corner. There they found her and dragged her away and took her to the water.

The mother cried and ran after them. But she could not catch up with them: the snakes had plunged into the water and taken Masha with them.

The mother wept for her daughter, thinking that surely she was dead.

Then one day, years later, as she was sitting by the window looking out toward the street, she suddenly saw Masha walking toward her, leading a little boy by the hand and carrying a baby girl.

The mother was filled with joy. She began to kiss Masha and ask her where she had been and whose children these were. Masha said that the children were hers, that the snake had taken her for his wife and she was now living with him in the watery kingdom.

The mother asked her whether she liked living in the watery kingdom. Masha said Yes, she liked it much better than on land.

Her mother asked her to stay with her, but Masha said No, she had promised her husband she would come back.

"And how are you going to get back home?" her mother asked.

"I'll go and I'll call, 'Osip! Osip! Come out and get me!' And he'll come out on the bank and take me away."

"All right," said her mother. "But you can at least spend the night with me."

Masha went to bed and fell asleep. Then the mother took an ax and went to the water's edge. "Osip! Osip!" she called. "Come on out!"

The snake swam up to the bank. Then the mother hit him with the ax and cut off his head. The water turned red with blood.

When her mother got back home, Masha woke up and said, "I'm going home, Mama. I don't feel right." Then she picked up her little girl and took her son by the hand and left.

When she came to the water's edge she called out, "Osip! Osip! Come out to me!" But nobody came.

She looked at the water and saw that it was red. And a snake's head was floating on it.

Then she kissed her daughter and her son and said to them, "You have no father, and soon you won't have a mother. You, my daughter, be a little swallow and fly over the water. You, my son, be a young nightingale and sing at twilight. And I'll be a cuckoo and cry for my husband who has been killed."

And they all flew off in different directions.

IVAN THE MERCHANT'S SON AND VASILISA THE WISE

PEASANT planted a field of rye, and it grew wondrous well—so thick and high he could hardly harvest it all. When he had brought in the last of the sheaves and threshed them, his granary was bulging full. "There!" he said to himself. "I'll have a good life for a change!"

But a little Mouse and a Sparrow took to visiting his granary. Four or five times every day, each of them would come to the granary, take some grain, and go back home with it—the Mouse back into his hole, and the Sparrow back up to his nest.

So the two of them had a good life for three whole years, eating their fill every day. Then the time came when the grain was almost gone. Noticing this, the Mouse decided to play a trick on the Sparrow and get the last of the grain for himself.

That night, while the Sparrow was asleep, the Mouse came to

32

the granary, gnawed a big hole in the floor, and pushed all the remaining grain down through the hole. When the Sparrow came the next morning for his breakfast, he found the bin quite empty. Hungry and angry, he flew away, saying to himself, "I've been insulted and cheated by that Mouse! I'll go to his King, the Lion, and make a complaint. I'll demand a fair trial of the case."

So off he flew to see the Lion. "O King of Beasts," he said to him, bowing low, "I have a complaint. For three years I lived in friendship with one of your beasts, a long-toothed Mouse. During all that time we ate from the same bin of grain, and never once did we quarrel. But then, when the grain began to run out, the Mouse played a trick on me. He gnawed a hole in the granary floor and took all the rest of the grain for himself, leaving me to go hungry. O King, please hear our case and judge justly! If not, I will fly to our King, the Eagle, and seek punitive justice."

"Well, fly along," said the Lion. "I don't care."

So the Sparrow flew to see the Eagle. After making a low bow, he told the Eagle his sad story: how the Mouse had filched the grain from him, and how the Lion had refused to prosecute the Mouse.

The Eagle waxed wroth. He immediately sent a herald to the Lion, with this message: "Gather all of your beasts together tomorrow. I will assemble all of my birds, and on such-and-such a field we will do battle."

The Lion had no choice. He sent out a call to all of his subject beasts, telling them to gather together to make war. He assembled a great many beasts—such a huge army of them that you couldn't see from one end of it to the other. As soon as they reached the field, the Eagle with all his subject birds descended upon them like a huge dark storm cloud, and the battle began.

They fought for three days and three nights, and the Eagle won; the field was piled high with the bodies of the dead beasts.

The Eagle dismissed all his subject birds, saying they could all go back home now. Then he himself flew off to the deep forest and perched in the top of a tall oak tree, wounded and exhausted. As he perched there, he pondered and pondered how to regain his lost strength.

Now, all this happened in ancient times. And in those same times there lived a young merchant and his wife, who had no children. One morning when the young merchant got up, he said to his wife, "I had a bad dream last night. I dreamed that a huge bird came to stay with us. He ate as much as a whole ox at once, and drank as much as a whole tubful of mead. There was no getting rid of him; we had to keep feeding him. Well, I think I'll go for a walk in the woods to cheer myself up."

He took his rifle and went into the woods. He went maybe a long way, maybe a short one, and came to the oak tree where the Eagle was perched. When he saw the Eagle, he took aim with his rifle.

But the Eagle cried out in a human voice, "Don't shoot me, brave fellow! You wouldn't gain much by that. Instead, take me home and feed me for three years, three months, and three days. If you do, my wings will mend, my strength will return, and I will repay you handsomely."

But the young merchant thought, "How can an Eagle repay anyone?" And again he raised his rifle.

The Eagle pleaded with him a second time, and a second time he lowered his gun. But after a moment, he once again took aim.

"Don't shoot me, brave fellow!" the Eagle said for the third time. "Feed me for three years, three months, and three days. If you do, my wings will mend, my strength will return, and I will repay you handsomely."

At this, the young merchant finally felt pity for the Eagle and took him home with him. He had an ox butchered, and a tub filled with mead, and gave them to the Eagle. "There!" he thought. "That should last him for a while!" But the Eagle ate and drank everything in a trice.

The merchant was having a hard time of it with his uninvited guest, who was eating him out of house and home. Seeing this, the Eagle said, "Master, if you will go out to the open fields, you will find a great many beasts there, killed or wounded. Take from them their valuable furs and sell them in the city. With the proceeds you get, you can feed both me and yourself and still have money to spare."

The young merchant went out to the open fields, where he found a great number of beasts, killed or wounded. He flayed them, took their valuable hides into town, and sold them for a large sum of money.

When one year had gone by, the Eagle told his host to take him to that part of the forest where the tall oaks stood. When they got there, the Eagle soared up into the sky, then came plunging down, and crashed breast-first into an oak tree. The tree split in two.

"Well," said the Eagle, "it seems I have not yet recovered my strength. Feed me for another whole year."

A second year went by, and again they went out to the great oaks. The Eagle soared up into the dark clouds, plummeted down, and crashed breast-first into a mighty oak tree. The tree broke into small pieces.

"Well," said the Eagle, "it seems I have still not recovered my strength. Feed me for another whole year."

When three years, three months, and three days had gone by, they went to the tall oaks again. The Eagle soared up higher than ever before, then swooped down on the biggest oak tree, and smashed it into tiny bits, from its tip to its roots, making the whole forest shake.

35

"Thank you, brave fellow," the Eagle said. "Now I have all my old strength back. Leave your horse here and get up on me. I'll take you to my own country and repay you for all your kindnesses."

The young merchant got on the Eagle's back and up they went —high into the sky, far above the blue sea.

"Look down at the blue sea below," the Eagle said. "Does it look big to you?"

"About as big as a wheel," said the merchant.

The Eagle gave a shake of his wings and let the merchant fall. Down, down he fell, and was filled with the fear of death. But before he fell into the sea the Eagle snatched him and soared up again. Up, up they went, even higher this time.

"Look down at the blue sea below," the Eagle said. "Does it look big to you?"

"About the size of a hen's egg."

The Eagle gave a shake of his wings and let the merchant fall again. Down, down he fell. But a second time the Eagle snatched him and soared back up. Up, up they went, higher than ever before.

"Look down at the blue sea below," the Eagle said. "Does it look big to you?"

"About the size of a poppy seed."

For a third time the Eagle gave a shake of his wings, and the merchant found himself falling. Down, down he fell, and was filled with the fear of death. But at the last moment the Eagle snatched him from above the waves.

"Well, my brave fellow," he asked, "now do you know what the fear of death is?"

"Now I know," the young merchant said. "I thought I would surely die."

36

"Well, just remember: I had the same thoughts when you aimed your gun at me."

The Eagle carried the merchant across the sea and straight to the Copper Kingdom. "My oldest sister lives here," he said. "While entertaining us as her guests, she will offer you gifts. But don't take any of them. Instead, ask for the copper casket."

Having said this, the Eagle flew down, struck the ground, and turned into a goodly youth. Then he and the young merchant entered the big courtyard of the sister's palace.

When she saw them, the sister was overjoyed. "Ah, brother mine! What wind blew thee here? It has been more than three years since I saw thee last! I thought thou hadst vanished completely. Well, tell me. What can I offer thee to eat and to drink?"

"Ask not of me, sister mine, for I need nothing. But ask that brave fellow there. He gave me food and drink for three years and kept me from dying of hunger."

The sister seated both of them at an oaken table bedecked with a finely embroidered cloth and gave them to eat and to drink. Afterward she took them to her treasure room and showed them wealth beyond measure. To the young merchant she said, "Here is gold and silver and precious stones. Take whatever your heart desires."

But the brave young merchant replied, "I need neither silver nor gold nor precious stones. Give me the copper casket."

"I should say not! That's a shoe that wouldn't fit the likes of you!"

At this, her brother grew angry. He turned himself into an Eagle, that swift-flying bird, snatched up the merchant, and rose from the earth.

"Brother mine! Dearest brother!" his sister cried out. "Come back! I'll give him the copper casket!"

"It's too late now, sister mine!" And the Eagle soared into the heavens.

"Take a look, my brave fellow, and say what you see behind us and ahead of us."

The young merchant looked, and said, "Behind us I see a fire. And ahead of us flowers are blooming."

"That fire is the Copper Kingdom burning. And ahead, flowers are blooming in the Silver Kingdom—the home of my second sister. While entertaining us as her guests, she will offer you gifts. But don't take any of them. Instead, ask for the silver casket."

The Eagle flew down to the ground, struck the damp earth, and turned into a goodly youth.

"Ah, brother mine!" his second sister greeted him. "Whence hast thou come? What befell thee? It has been a long time since thou wast here. And what can I offer thee to eat and to drink?"

"Ask not of me, sister mine, for I need nothing. But ask that brave fellow there. He gave me food and drink for three years and kept me from dying of hunger."

The second sister seated both of them at an oaken table bedecked with a fine, embroidered cloth, and gave them to eat and to drink. Then she took them to her treasure room. "Here is gold and silver and precious stones," she said to the young merchant. "Take whatever your heart desires."

"I need neither gold nor silver nor precious stones. Give me the silver casket."

"No, brave young fellow, that mouthful is not for you! You might choke on it!"

At this, her brother grew angry. He turned himself into an Eagle, that swift-flying bird, snatched up the merchant, and rose into the air.

"Brother mine! Dearest brother! Come back! I'll give him the box!"

"It's too late, sister mine!" And once again the Eagle soared up into the heavens.

"Take a look, my brave fellow, and say what you see behind us and ahead of us."

"Behind us I see a fire. And ahead, flowers are blooming."

"That fire is the Silver Kingdom burning. And those flowers are blooming in the Golden Kingdom—the home of my youngest sister. While entertaining us as her guests, she will offer you gifts. But don't take any of them. Instead, ask for the golden casket."

The Eagle came down to the earth, struck it, and turned into a goodly youth.

"Ah, brother mine!" the youngest sister exclaimed. "Whence comest thou? What befell thee? Why hast thou not come to see me in such a long time? Well, what can I offer thee to eat and to drink?"

"Ask not of me, sister mine, for I need nothing: I'm my own man. But ask that brave fellow there. He gave me food and drink for three years and kept me from dying of hunger."

The youngest sister seated them at her table, as the two older sisters had done before her. When they had eaten and drunk their fill, she took them to her treasure room and offered the young merchant gold and silver and precious stones. "I don't need any of those things," he replied. "Just give me the golden casket."

"Here, take it for good luck," said she. "You gave my brother food and drink for three years and kept him from dying of hunger. And, for my brother's sake, there is nothing I would spare."

So the young merchant stayed there in the Golden Kingdom, feasting and making merry, until the time came for him to set out for home.

"Farewell," the Eagle said to him. "Please don't think ill of me. And remember: Don't open the casket until you are home."

The young merchant set out. He traveled maybe a long way, maybe a short one, and felt a need to rest.

He stopped in a meadow which happened to be in the realm of the King of the Unbaptized Brow. There he took out the golden casket and looked at it. He looked and looked. Finally, his curiosity became too much for him, and he opened it.

At once, a great palace rose up in front of him, cunningly ornamented. And a throng of servants appeared, asking, "What is your wish, Sire? What are your commands?"

The merchant, that brave young fellow, ate and drank his fill, and then went to bed.

When the King of the Unbaptized Brow saw the great palace on his lands, he sent envoys. "Find out," he instructed them, "who is this fool who has come to my realm and built a palace without my permission. Then tell him to depart in good time, while his skin is yet whole!"

When the young merchant heard these dire words he began to puzzle and ponder how to get the palace back into the casket. He thought long and hard but could not figure it out.

"I would be glad to move away," he told the envoys, "but I can't figure out how to do it."

The envoys went back to the King of the Unbaptized Brow and reported what the merchant had said.

"Tell him," said the King, "to give me that which is in his home unbeknownst to him, and I will put the palace back in his casket."

The young merchant had no choice. He solemnly promised to give the King of the Unbaptized Brow that which was in his home unbeknownst to him. Immediately, on the King's orders, the palace disappeared into the golden casket. The merchant picked up the casket and went on his way.

After a short time, or maybe a long one, he arrived home. "Welcome home, my love," said his wife. "Where hast thou been?"

"Wherever I was, I'm not there now."

"I have a surprise for thee. While thou wast away, God gave us a baby boy."

"So!" thought the merchant. "*That's* what was in my home unbeknownst to me!" And he began to grieve and to sorrow deeply.

"What can be the matter?" asked his wife. "Art thou not gladdened at being home?"

"The matter is something else," he replied. Then he told her of what had happened, and both of them wept and grieved together.

But one cannot weep for a lifetime. After a while, the merchant opened the casket, and lo! a huge palace rose up before them, cunningly ornamented.

So the young merchant and his wife and baby son began to live in the palace and prosper. The boy, whose name was Ivan, grew to be strong and clever, and became a goodly youth.

One morning, some ten years and more after the merchant's return, the boy Ivan awoke feeling sad. He said to his father, "Father mine, I had a bad dream. I dreamed that the King of the Unbaptized Brow commanded that I come to him. He said he had waited for me a long time and would not wait any longer."

Ivan's father and mother wept at this news. Then they gave him their parental blessing and sent him off.

He traveled along the broad roads, through the untrodden fields and the wide, open plains, and finally came to a deep forest where there was no sign of human life. There, in a clearing, he saw a little hut on hen's legs, facing the woods with its back toward him.

He called out:

Little hut, I pray thee!
Turn thy back to the woods and thy front to me!

Obediently, the little hut turned its front to Ivan the Merchant's Son, and its back to the woods. Ivan went in. And there, lying on the floor, was Baba-Yaga of the Bony Nose.

When she saw Ivan, she said, "Foo! Foo! I never heard tell of a Russian, and none did I ever see. Yet here is a Russian right before me! Whence comest thou, goodly youth, and whither wendest thy way?"

"Thou old witch! What dost mean asking news of a wayfarer without first giving him to eat and to drink?"

Baba-Yaga placed food and drink on the table. Then, when Ivan the Merchant's Son had eaten and drunk his fill, she made ready a bed for him.

Early the next morning she awakened him and began again with her questions. Ivan told her all, and then he said, "Grand-mother, what way must I go to reach the King of the Unbaptized Brow?"

"It is well," said she, "that thou camest to me. Otherwise, thou wouldst not yet be alive. The King of the Unbaptized Brow is wroth with thee because thou art tardy in coming to him. Now here is what thou must do. Follow this path until thou reachest a pond, then take cover behind a tree and wait. Soon three doves will fly down and alight on the shore. These are the King's three daughters. One of them has speckled wings. When they take off their wings and their clothing to go bathing in the pond, wait for thy chance and then seize the wings of the speckled dove. Keep them and do not yield them up until she promises to marry thee. Then all will turn out well for thee."

Ivan the Merchant's Son bade farewell to Baba-Yaga and went off along the path.

He walked and walked until he came to the pond, where he hid himself behind a big tree. Very soon, three doves flew down and alighted on the shore. One of the three had speckled wings. The doves struck the ground and turned into three beautiful maidens. Then they took off their wings and their clothing, and went into the water to bathe.

Ivan awaited his chance, then crept out and seized the speckled wings. Back behind his tree, he waited to see what would happen.

When the three maidens had finished bathing, they came out of the water, and two of them, donning their clothing and wings, immediately flew away. But the third remained behind, seeking her missing wings. As she searched, she said aloud, "Tell me please tell me, who took my wings? If he's old, he can be a grandfather to me. If he's of middle age, he can be my uncle. And if he is young, I will marry him."

Ivan the Merchant's Son stepped out from behind the tree. "Here are thy wings," he said.

"Well, goodly youth and husband-to-be, tell me now: What is thy family? And whither wendest thy way?"

"I am Ivan the Merchant's Son, on my way to see thy father, the King of the Unbaptized Brow."

"And I am Vasilisa the Wise."

Vasilisa the Wise was the King's favorite daughter, being not only wise but beautiful. When she had told her betrothed how to reach her father's realm, she flew off, in the form of a dove, after her sisters.

When Ivan reached her father's palace, the King put him to work as a scullion—working in the kitchen, cutting wood and bringing it in, and hauling water. The cook, whose name was Chumichka, took a dislike to Ivan and complained about him to the King.

"Your Majesty," he said, "Ivan the Merchant's Son has made a

44

great boast. He boasts that in only one night he can cut down a great forest, chop up the trees, dig up the roots, plow the ground, plant wheat, harvest it, thresh it, grind it into flour, and from that flour make pies for Your Majesty's breakfast."

"Very well," said the King. "Send him to me."

When Ivan appeared before him, the King said, "I've been told of your boast that in one single night you can cut down a great forest, plow up the ground as though it were an open field, plant wheat, harvest it, and grind it into flour, and from that flour bake pies for my breakfast. Why must you boast like that? Now you'll have to do all these things by tomorrow morning. And see that you don't fail!"

However much Ivan denied that he had made such a boast, it availed him nothing. He left the King's presence with his troubled head hung low in grief. Princess Vasilisa the Wise saw him and asked, "Why art so melancholy?"

"What need to tell thee? There is naught thou canst do to allay my grief!"

"How canst thou be certain? Perhaps I can help."

Ivan told her of the task laid upon him by the King of the Unbaptized Brow.

"What kind of a task is that? Only a tiny one. The great task will come later. Go to bed now and sleep. The morning is wiser than the evening. By morning, everything will have been done."

Just at midnight Vasilisa the Wise stepped out on her beautiful veranda and uttered a call in a loud voice. In a moment, from every direction, workmen appeared—so many the eye could not take them all in. Some of them set about felling trees, others digging up roots, and still others plowing the ground. While some of them were planting in one part of the field, others were already reaping in another part, and still others were grinding the grain into flour. The dust from the flour-milling rose up in a cloud, and by morning all the grain had been milled and the pies baked. Ivan brought the pies to the King of the Unbaptized Brow for his breakfast.

"Very good!" said the King. And he commanded that Ivan be given a reward from his treasury.

Chumichka the cook became even more angry at Ivan than before, and again complained to the King. "Your Majesty," he said, "Ivan the Merchant's Son boasts that he can build, in one single night, a ship that will fly through the air."

"Very well. Send him to me."

When Ivan appeared, the King said, "Why do you boast to my servants that in one night you can build a ship that will fly through the air, and yet tell me nothing about it? Now you must do it by morning. And see to it that you don't fail!"

Ivan the Merchant's Son walked away with his troubled head hanging far down on his chest. He felt very badly out of sorts.

Vasilisa the Wise saw him, and asked, "Why art so sad and melancholy?"

"Why shouldn't I be? The King has commanded me to build, in one night, a ship that will fly through the air."

"What kind of a task is that? Only a tiny one. The great task will come later. Go to bed now and sleep. The morning is wiser than the evening. By morning, everything will have been done."

At midnight Vasilisa the Wise stepped out on her beautiful veranda and uttered a call in a loud voice. In a moment, from every direction, carpenters appeared. They set to work with their axes, hewing away at a furious rate, and by morning everything was ready.

"Very good!" said the King to Ivan. "And now, let's go for a ride!"

The two of them got in, and for a third they took along Chumichka the cook. As they flew through the sky they passed over the wild-game preserve. The cook leaned over the side to look, and Ivan gave him a shove. Out he fell—down among the wild beasts, who tore him into small pieces.

"Oh!" Ivan cried out. "Chumichka has fallen overboard!"

"The devil with him!" said the King. "A dog should meet a dog's death!"

When they came back to the palace, the King said, "Ivan, you are a sly fellow. Now here is a third task for you. I want you to break a wild stallion for me. If you break him, I'll give my daughter to you in marriage."

"Well, that's easy to do," thought Ivan. And he went away from the King, laughing to himself.

Vasilisa the Wise saw him and questioned him about all that had taken place. Then she said, "Thou art not so clever, Ivan. The task that has just been assigned to thee is a great one, because the stallion is the King of the Unbaptized Brow himself. He will carry thee through the sky, above the motionless forest, and below the moving clouds, and scatter thy bones in the open fields. Go to the blacksmith without delay, and tell him to make for thee a hammer of iron weighing a hundred pounds. When thou mountest the stallion, cling to him fast, and strike him on the head with the iron hammer."

The next morning the wild stallion was brought out of the stables. The grooms could hardly hold him. He snorted, threw himself this way and that, and reared up on his hind legs. No sooner had Ivan mounted him than he flew up over the motionless forest and below the moving clouds, and raced through the sky more swiftly than a strong wind. But Ivan held on tight and kept hitting him on the head with his hammer. The stallion, exhausted, came down to the ground. Ivan handed him over to the stable boys and went for a rest.

When he came to the palace he was met by the King, wearing

a bandage on his unbaptized brow. "I have broken the stallion, Your Majesty," he said.

"Very well. Come tomorrow to select your bride. Right now I have a headache."

In the morning, Vasilisa the Wise said to Ivan, "My father has three daughters. He will turn us into mares and tell thee to make thy choice. Look carefully, and thou willst see that on my bridle one of the spangles is tarnished. Then he will transform us into doves. My sisters will quietly peck at the buckwheat in front of them, but I shall keep flapping my wings. The third time, he will make us appear as three maidens, alike in face, figure, and hair. But I shall wave my kerchief, and by this sign thou shalt know me."

Just as she had said, the King brought out three mares, one just like another, and had them lined up.

"Choose the one you like best," he said to Ivan.

Ivan looked closely. On the bridle of one of the mares, a spangle was tarnished. He took hold of the bridle and said, "This one will be my bride."

"You chose the worst one. You could have done better," said the King.

"It doesn't matter. This one will do."

"Choose again," said the King, and he brought forth three identical doves and tossed some buckwheat in front of them. Ivan noticed that one of them kept flapping her wings, and he caught hold of her. "This is my bride," he said.

"You've bit off more than you can chew. Try again."

The King brought forth three maidens—alike in face, figure, and hair. Ivan saw that one of them was waving her handkerchief. He took her by the hand, saying, "This is my bride."

That settled it. The King of the Unbaptized Brow had to give Vasilisa the Wise to Ivan in marriage.

The wedding was a merry one. Neither a long time nor a short time thereafter, Ivan the Merchant's Son decided to flee with Vasilisa the Wise and take her back to his own country. Their horses were saddled, and in the dark of night they left.

The next morning, the King of the Unbaptized Brow realized what had happened and sent pursuers after them.

"Bend thine ear down to the ground," said Vasilisa the Wise to her husband Ivan, "and tell me what thou hearest."

Ivan bent his ear to the ground, listened, and said, "I hear the neighing of horses."

Vasilisa the Wise turned him into a vegetable garden, and herself into a cabbage head. The pursuers came back to the King with empty hands. "Your Majesty," they reported, "in the open field we saw nothing but a vegetable garden and a cabbage head."

"Go back and bring me that cabbage head," he commanded. "Those two are becoming very clever."

Again the pursuers set out, and again Ivan bent his ear to the ground.

"I hear the whinnying of horses," he said.

Vasilisa the Wise turned him into a well and herself into a bright falcon. The falcon sat on the edge of the well and drank from it.

The pursuers rode up to the well. Seeing that the road ended there, they turned back. "Your Majesty," they reported, "in the open field we saw nothing but a well with a bright falcon drinking out of it."

At this, the King of the Unbaptized Brow went off himself in pursuit.

"Bend thine ear to the ground and tell me what thou hearest," said Vasilisa the Wise to her husband Ivan.

"Ach! I hear a trampling and pounding much louder than before!"

"That is my father pursuing us. I don't know what to do. I can think of nothing."

"And I can think of even less."

Vasilisa the Wise had three things with her: a brush, a comb, and a towel. Now she bethought herself of them and said, "I have a way of protecting us against the King of the Unbaptized Brow."

She threw the brush behind her, and a thick forest sprang up— so thick and so great that a man could not cut his way through, and in three years could not get around it. But the King of the Unbaptized Brow gnawed and gnawed at the thick forest, making a path for himself. He got through and came hot on their heels.

When he was almost within reach. Vasilisa the Wise threw her comb behind her, and a huge mountain rose up—too high to climb and too big to go around.

But the King of the Unbaptized Brow dug and dug at the mountain, cut a way through for himself, and came after them once again.

Then Vasilisa the Wise threw her towel behind her, and a vast, boundless ocean appeared. The King came racing up to the shore, saw he could go no farther, and turned back toward home.

When Ivan the Merchant's Son and Vasilisa the Wise came near to Ivan's home country, he said, "I'll go on ahead and tell my father and mother about thee. Meantime, do thou wait for me here."

"When thou hast reached home and art kissing all of thy kin," said Vasilisa the Wise, "take care not to kiss thy godmother. For if thou dost, thou shalt forget me."

Ivan the Merchant's Son, when he reached home, kissed everyone joyfully, including his godmother—and so he forgot all about Vasilisa the Wise.

As for her, she stayed there on the road, poor thing, waiting for Ivan to come after her. She waited and waited, but Ivan the Merchant's Son never came for her.

Finally she went into the city and hired out as a servant in an old lady's house. Ivan, meanwhile, had decided to marry. He selected a bride and then held a feast to which everyone was invited.

When Vasilisa the Wise learned of it, she dressed herself as a beggar woman and went to the house of Ivan's parents to ask for alms.

"Wait," said Ivan's mother, the merchant's wife, "and I'll bake you a little pie. I won't cut you a slice from the big one."

"I thank thee most heartily, ma'am, for the little one," said Vasilisa the Wise.

But the big pie came out of the oven scorched, while the little one was just right. So Ivan's mother gave Vasilisa the scorched pie and set the little one on the table for the feast.

When the little pie was cut, two doves flew out of it. "Kiss me," said the he-dove to the she-dove.

"No, I won't," said the she-dove. "You'll forget me, just as Ivan the Merchant's Son forgot Vasilisa the Wise."

A second time, and then a third time, the he-dove said, "Kiss me!" And a second time, and then a third time, the she-dove replied, "No, I won't. You'll forget me, just as Ivan the Merchant's Son forgot Vasilisa the Wise."

Ivan the Merchant's Son came to his senses, recognized who the beggar woman was, and said to his father, his mother, and all the guests, "There is my bride!"

"Well, if you have a wife, then live with her!"

The newly selected bride was given rich gifts and sent back home. Ivan the Merchant's Son and Vasilisa the Wise began to live together and prosper, and they always avoided evil.

51

THE SHREWISH WIFE

CERTAIN MAN had a wife who made every day of his life miserable. She was always nagging at him. And of all the contrary women on this earth, she was the worst. Whenever he dared to suggest anything, she would snap back, "A lot you know about it, you fool!" And then she would do just the opposite of what he wanted. If he said he thought she was getting sick and should take a pill, she would sneer, "Nonsense! I don't need any pill!" And the next day she'd be sick in bed. If he said she looked well, she would growl, "A lot you know about it! I feel miserable!" Then she would take a whole handful of pills, and really get sick. Sometimes, on a Monday, he would meekly suggest, "I don't think you should do the washing today. It looks like rain." Without so much as a glance at the weather outside, she would snap, "Oh, is that so?" Then she would do the washing, and end by hanging up the clothes on the line in a heavy rain.

One day this man and his wife were out picking green raspberries. (They were picking them green because that morning the

52

man had said the raspberries wouldn't be ripe for another week. To which his wife had replied, "A lot you know about it! We'll pick them today!") Now, right in the middle of the berry patch there was a big, deep pit with only a narrow opening at the top. The opening was concealed by the thick raspberry bushes, and the man hadn't even known the pit was there until one time when he almost fell into it.

Seeing his wife getting close to the middle of the berry patch, he called to her, "Don't go any farther! There's a big hole just in front of you!" "Nonsense!" she yelled back at him, and kept right on going until *plop!* down she fell into the deep, dark pit.

The man ran to the edge and looked down. He could see only darkness, and he heard no sound.

He stood there for a while, feeling sad. Then he shrugged his shoulders and headed for home.

The next few days were the most peaceful he had ever known in his life. Then late one night he was awakened in the middle of a sound slumber by a knock at the door. When he opened it, there stood an imp. Usually, imps are scarey. But this one was not so much scarey as scared. His horns looked limp, and he kept twitching his tail nervously.

"Well, what do *you* want?" the man asked him.

"That woman down there in the pit—is that your wife?"

In his heart, the man was glad to learn his wife was alive. But he didn't let on to the imp. "Yes," he said gruffly, "it is. So?"

"Well," said the imp, "from the moment she fell down there among us devils, she has been making life miserable for us. It's sheer torment. Everything we do she finds fault with. Nag, nag, nag—that's all she does. We just can't stand it anymore. For the love of Satan, take her back!"

"Why should I? She made *my* life hell on earth. Now let her make your life earth in hell."

The imp grew desperate. "Please!" he begged. "We've already had more than we can bear! We'll give you anything if you'll just get her out of there!"

"A full bag of gold?"

"A full bag of gold."

"And no cheating tricks?"

"No cheating tricks. I promise."

"Well," the man said, hesitating, "I'll think about it."

Just as he uttered these words, whom should he see coming up the porch steps but his wife! The imp saw her, too, and with one loud yowl, he fled.

The next morning the man found a full bag of gold on the porch. All the rest of his life, he wondered why the imp had left it, since he had done nothing to get his wife out of the pit—she had managed to climb out herself, with the help of a very long tree root. But the reason was simple. The imp was afraid that if he didn't give the man the gold, his wife would come down to get it.

THE THIEF

N OLD MAN and his old wife had a son named Klimka. They thought and thought about what trade he should take up and finally decided to apprentice him to a thief.

Klimka lived with the master thief for maybe a long time, maybe a short one. (A tale is told quickly, from first to last, but a deed is never accomplished so fast.) He learned how to steal in splendid style. But the one thing he hadn't learned yet was how to filch eggs from a magpie's nest.

"Come along," the master thief said to him, "and I'll show you how to filch eggs from a magpie. I'd also show you how to steal the pants off a living man, but I myself don't know how."

Then the master thief climbed up a tree. He didn't succeed in stealing the magpie's eggs. But as he was climbing, Klimka succeeded in stealing his pants off him.

"There's nothing more I can teach you," the master thief said. "You're already teaching me!"

So Klimka went back to live with his father and mother and began to support them by stealing. Whatever he laid eyes upon, he would filch and take home to the hut. If the women of the village hung out their husbands' shirts to dry after a washing,

56

he would steal the shirts. If they put unbleached linen out to bleach, he would take that, too.

One day all the peasants in the village held a general meeting and complained to the barin. "A certain Klimka, a thief," they said, "has appeared among us. He has filched all the rich peasants' property and stolen the poor ones blind."

"Why don't you catch him, you simpletons?" the barin asked.

"He's not the kind you can catch," they replied. "He's so clever and sly, he could steal the eggs out from under a bird."

The barin decided he would like to test Klimka's boldness and skill. He sent for him, and when he arrived, he asked him: "Can you steal a ram from me?"

"Yes, I can," Klimka said.

The barin ordered his shepherds to guard all the rams in their flocks against Klimka. Then they set off to drive their flocks out to pasture. Klimka ran ahead of them. He had a rope and with it he made a noose, a very tricky one—you could hang with it around your neck, yet it wouldn't hang you. Klimka climbed up a birch tree, put the noose around his neck, and then dangled there as if he had hanged himself.

When the shepherds saw him, they thought surely he was dead and left off guarding their flocks carefully. As soon as they had gone by, Klimka jumped down from the tree and ran ahead again. He climbed up an ash tree, put the noose around his neck, and once more let himself dangle.

The shepherds came up to him, took one look, and cried out, "Klimka the thief is hanging here, too!" "Yes," said one of them, "he's hanged himself on the ash tree." But another said, "Nonsense! That's not Klimka. He hanged himself on that birch tree back there."

They argued and argued and finally made a bet. Then they

ran back to see who it was dangling from the birch tree. While they were gone, Klimka jumped down to the ground, grabbed a ram by the horns, and was off to the tavern.

The next morning the barin sent for him. "Did you steal the ram?" he asked.

"Yes, I did."

"Where is it now?"

"I sold it."

"And where is the money?"

"I spent it on drink."

"Well, now let's see if you can steal my cash box and all the money in it."

"With pleasure!"

The barin took his cash box and put it right next to the window, on purpose. Then he got his rifle and gave swords to his servants. "Just let that Klimka stick his head in here," he told them, "and we'll give him the kind of reception he deserves!"

That night Klimka stole a goat. Then he went to the window, opened it, stuck the goat's head inside, and made it look straight at the barin.

Both the barin and his servants thought it was the Devil himself. Dropping the rifle and swords, they fell to the floor in a faint, as Klimka grabbed the cash box and was off and away.

The next morning the barin sent for Klimka again.

"Did you make off with my cash box?"

"Yes, I did."

"Where is it now?"

"It's broken."

"And where is the money?"

"I gambled it away and spent it on drink."

"Well, now let's see if you can steal my horse."

"With pleasure!"

The barin commanded his stable boys to guard his horse like the apple of their eyes. He ordered one of them to hold the horse by the tail, another to hold him by the bridle, and a third to mount on his back. Two others were told to stand guard at the stable door.

Meantime Klimka got hold of some of the barin's clothes and put them on. As soon as night fell, he came to the stable. "Are you here, fellows?" he called out, changing his voice to make it sound like the barin's.

"Yes, sir!" they replied.

"You must be almost frozen."

"Oh, yes, sir! We are!"

"Well, here's a little vodka to warm you up. Just be sure, though, to keep a close watch!"

"Yes, sir, we'll do our best!"

Klimka plied them with vodka, and soon they were all quite drunk. Then he took the one sitting on the horse and put him astride a crossbeam in the barn. He took the bridle away from the one who was holding it and put a piece of rope in his hand. To the one who was holding the horse's tail, he gave a handful of straw instead. As for the two guards at the stable door, he tied them together by the hair of their heads. Then he leaped up on the horse, gave him a flick of the whip, and was off and away.

In the morning, when the barin came out to the stable, he saw his horse had been stolen and found the stable boys in a drunken sleep. He started to shout and stamp his feet, and then what an uproar there was! One stable boy fell off the crossbeam and knocked all his insides out. Another, still half-asleep, was mumbling, "Whoa, you old nag! Whoa!" And the two that were tied together by the hair of their heads started a tug of war, then began flailing away at each other with their fists.

The barin spat and turned his back on the whole disgusting scene. Then he sent for Klimka.

"Did you steal my horse?"

"Yes, I did."

"Where is it?"

"I sold it."

"Where is the money?"

"I gambled it away and spent it on drink."

"Well, go to the Devil!"

SISTER ALIONUSHKA AND BROTHER IVANUSHKA

N OLD MAN and an old woman had two children, a girl named Alionushka and a little boy named Ivanushka. Before Alionushka was fully grown her old parents died, leaving her and Ivanushka all alone in the world.

She set out to look for work, taking her little brother with her. They walked a long way across the wide fields, and Ivanushka became thirsty. "Sister," he said, "give me some water to drink."

"Just be patient, Ivanushka," she told him. "Soon we'll come to a well."

They walked on and on, but no well came into sight. The sun rose higher and higher in the sky. It was very hot, and the children's throats were parched and dry.

Then Ivanushka saw the hoofprint of a cow with some water

left in it from the rain that had fallen the night before. "Sister," he said, "I want to drink some of that water."

"No, little brother, you mustn't. If you do, you'll become a calf."

Ivanushka obeyed her, and on they walked. The sun rose still higher, the day got still hotter, and the children began to sweat. Then Ivanushka saw a horse's hoofprint full of water. "Sister," he said, "I'm going to drink some of that water."

"No, little brother, you mustn't. If you do, you'll become a colt."

Ivanushka sighed, but again he obeyed, and on they went.

The sun rose to high noon, the children were drenched with sweat, and their throats were so dry they could hardly speak. Then Ivanushka saw the hoofprint of a goat with water standing in it. "Sister," said he, "I'm so thirsty I just can't stand it. I'm going to drink that water."

"No, little brother, you mustn't. If you do, you'll become a baby goat."

But this time Ivanushka didn't obey her: he drank the water in the goat's hoofprint. And when he had drunk it all, he turned into a little goat.

"Ivanushka!" Alionushka called. But instead of her brother, a little white goat came running up to her.

Alionushka sat down by a haystack and cried. All the while, the little goat gamboled around her.

She was still sitting there when a merchant came by on the road. Seeing Alionushka, he called out, "Pretty maiden, why are you crying?"

Alionushka told him of her misfortunes. When she had finished, he said, "Marry me. I'll dress you in silver and gold. And the little goat can live with us."

Alionushka thought and thought about it and finally decided to marry the merchant.

Their wedded life started out happily. And the little goat lived with them, drinking from the same cup and eating from the same dish as Alionushka.

Then one day when the merchant was away from home, a witch appeared from out of nowhere. She stood under Alionushka's window and coaxed her to come out and go for a swim in the river.

When they reached the riverbank, the witch held Alionushka

fast, tied a big stone around her neck, and threw her into the water. Then she turned herself into Alionushka, put on her clothes, and returned to the house.

Nobody there could tell that the witch was not really Alionushka. Not even the merchant, when he returned home, knew she was a witch instead of his wife. Only the little goat knew.

He hung his head low and would neither eat nor drink. Each morning and evening he would go along the river bank, calling out:

> *Alionushka, sister dear!*
> *Come out of the water. Come here!*

The witch heard about it and told her supposed husband to slaughter the little goat. The merchant did not want to do it, since he was fond of the goat. But the witch kept insisting, until finally the merchant said, "All right. I'll have him slaughtered."

The witch ordered the servants to build a big fire, heat up an iron cauldron, and sharpen the knives.

The little goat, who could tell he did not have much longer to live, went to the merchant and said, "Before I die, let me go once more to the river to drink the water and rinse out my insides."

"All right," said the merchant. "Go on."

The goat ran to the bank of the river and called out in a plaintive voice:

> *Alionushka, sister dear!*
> *Come out of the water. Come here!*
> *The flames leap high.*
> *The cauldron is hot.*
> *The knives are sharpened.*
> *They'll cut my throat.*

64

And Alionushka answered him from the river:

O Ivanushka, brother mine!
A heavy stone is weighing me down!
The silken grass has my legs entwined.
And my breast is buried in golden sands.

The witch, who had been looking for the goat, summoned a servant and said, "Go find the little goat and bring him here."

The servant went to the riverbank, and there he found the little goat running back and forth and calling out:

Alionushka, sister dear!
Come out of the water. Come here!
The flames leap high.
The cauldron is hot.
The knives are sharpened.
They'll cut my throat.

And from the river came the reply:

O Ivanushka, brother mine!
A heavy stone is weighing me down!
The silken grass has my legs entwined.
And my breast is buried in golden sands.

The servant ran back and told the merchant what he had seen and heard. Everyone in the household hurried to the river. They threw out a silken net and brought Alionushka to the bank. They took the stone from around her neck, washed her in spring water, and dressed her in fine clothes. She came to life and was more beautiful than ever before.

Out of sheer joy, the little goat turned three somersaults, and immediately turned back into Ivanushka.

But the evil witch was tied to a horse's tail and dragged through the wide open fields.

N A CERTAIN PART of Russia there lived two brothers, one rich and the other poor. One day the poor brother came to the rich brother and asked if he could borrow his horse to haul some wood he was going to cut in the forest. The rich brother lent him the horse, but without any harness. What could the poor brother do? He decided to hitch the horse to the cart by his tail. Then he went to the forest and cut a big cartload of wood. It was such a big load, in fact, that when he got home with it and started through the gate, the cart got stuck. The horse pulled hard, with a jerk, and off came his tail.

When the poor brother brought the horse back without any tail, the rich brother got very angry and said, "For that, I'll take you to Shemyaka the Judge!"

So off they went. After going a long way, they stopped for the night at the house of another wealthy peasant. While the two rich men sat at the table together, eating and drinking and

67

making merry, the poor man lay hungry on the stove-bed.* Curious to see what the rich men were eating, he leaned over the edge of the bed. But he leaned too far over and fell, crushing to death the baby asleep in the crib below.

The rich peasant, the baby's father, cried, "I'll take you to Shemyaka the Judge for that!"

So off went the three of them. Along the way, they came to a high bridge—a kind of overpass with another road running beneath it. The poor man said to himself, "Any way you look at it, I'm done for. I might as well jump off this bridge and kill myself."

But down on the road below, a young fellow was driving a cart, taking his sick father to the bathhouse. When the poor man jumped, he landed right on top of the old man and crushed him to death.

"I'll go and complain about this to Shemyaka the Judge," said the young fellow.

When they got to Judge Shemyaka's, the first to make his complaint was the rich brother, who told how his horse had lost its tail. While he was talking, the poor brother took a rock he had picked up and wrapped it in his handkerchief. Then, standing behind his brother, he held it up so the judge could see it. "If Judge Shemyaka doesn't decide in my favor," he said to himself, "I'll bash his head in!"

But Judge Shemyaka thought that what the poor man was showing him was money—a hundred rubles in coins wrapped in the handkerchief. So he ruled that the rich brother should let the poor brother keep his horse until its tail had grown back.

* A broad wooden shelf up close to the ceiling in a Russian peasant cottage, extending from the stove to the opposite wall, and used as a bed.

The next to make a complaint was the rich peasant whose baby had been crushed to death. Once again, the poor man held up the rock wrapped in the handkerchief. Judge Shemyaka then ordered the rich peasant, "Let this man have your wife until she has another baby."

Finally, the young fellow made his complaint about how his father had been killed. Once again, the poor man held up his rock. Said Judge Shemyaka to him, "You go and stand under that bridge." And to the young fellow, he said, "And you can jump off the bridge and kill him."

When the others had left, Judge Shemyaka called the poor man to him and demanded his money. The latter took the rock out of the handkerchief and showed it to the judge. "If you hadn't decided in my favor," said he, "I'd have bashed your head in."

Judge Shemyaka crossed himself. "Thank God I decided the right way!" he exclaimed.

The next day the poor man came to his rich brother to get his horse, as the judge had ruled. "Instead of my horse," proposed the rich brother, "let me give you five rubles, three bushels of grain, and a goat. And may there be peace between us forever."

The poor brother took all these things; then he went to the wealthy peasant to get his wife, as Judge Shemyaka had ruled, and keep her until she had another child.

"Instead of my wife," pleaded the rich peasant, "let me give you fifty rubles, a cow with her calf, a mare with her colt, and four bushels of grain. And may there be peace between us forever."

The poor man took all these things, and then went to see the young fellow, saying, "Judge Shemyaka ruled that I must stand under the bridge, and you must jump down from it and crush me to death."

69

But the young fellow was afraid of making the jump. He begged, "Instead of that, let me give you two hundred rubles, a horse, and five bushels of grain. And may there be peace between us forever."

So the poor man took all these things and was rich for the rest of his life.

THE MONASTERY OF NO CARES

T THE TIME of our tale, the Tsar who ruled Russia was known for his great curiosity. His curiosity, moreover, was of a strange kind. He was eager to learn all he could about *things*—everything he laid eyes on, in fact. But he wasn't very much interested in *people*. Indeed, he frequently forgot the names—and even the faces—of people he saw quite often.

On one of his many travels through the Russian realm, as he was passing through a small town, he was struck by the handsome appearance of its monastery. Ordering his equipage to make a halt, he went inside, where he found even more to admire than he had seen from the outside.

Very pleased, he asked the Prior, "What is the name of your monastery?"

"Its name is perhaps not entirely fitting for an abode of monks," answered the Prior, "but since long before my time it has been called the Monastery of No Cares."

The Tsar gave a short laugh. "In that case," he said, "I'll give you and your monks something to worry about."

"And what might that be?"

"When I pass this way again, as I shall soon, I will ask you for the answers to three riddles. First, since your prayers bring you so close to God, you must tell me how many stars there are in the heavens. Second, you must tell me the value of my person—what price I would bring if sold on the market. And third, you must tell me what I am thinking at that very moment." With this, the Tsar took his departure.

That same evening, the Prior assembled all of his learned monks, and they tried to solve the riddles. But no one could answer them. On the following evening they gathered together again, but with no better results. And so it went for a week.

Now, at the Monastery of No Cares it was the custom every evening for the cook to inquire of the Prior what food was to be prepared for the morrow. On one such occasion, having received his instructions, the cook said to the Prior, "Father, I would like to ask a question that has nothing to do with preparing food."

"Ask, my son," said the Prior.

"Well," began the cook, "ever since I have been a monk here, our monastery has been free of cares. And I'm told it was always that way here, even in ancient times. But for an entire week now, you and the other learned brethren have been worried. Dare I ask why?"

"Of course," answered the Prior. And he told the cook about the Tsar's riddles.

"Father," said the cook, when the Prior had told him, "I can answer those questions to the Tsar's satisfaction. But I can do it only if you will allow me to put on your vestments and greet him when he returns here."

The Prior agreed. A few days later the Tsar passed that way again, returning from a journey to a remote part of Russia. He was greeted at the monastery gate by the cook, wearing the vestments of the Prior. With his poor memory for faces, and his good memory for things, the Tsar recognized only the costume and not the person wearing it.

When they had exchanged greetings, the Tsar asked, "Have you solved my riddles?"

"Yes," said the cook, "I have."

"Well, then, tell me. How many stars are there in the heavens?"

"A trillion trillion, a billion billion, and a million million."

"Are you sure that is correct?"

"If you don't believe it, try counting them yourself."

The Tsar was nonplused, but he didn't show it. Without so much as the flicker of an eye, he next asked, "And what is the value of my person?"

"You are our earthly Sovereign," the cook replied, "but we also have one in Heaven. If He could be sold for thirty pieces of silver, you could be sold for half that price."

"Very well," said the Tsar. He was quite disgruntled, but sure he would catch the Prior on the last riddle. "Now tell me," he said, "what am I thinking at this moment?"

"You think you are talking to the Prior," the cook said, "but you are really talking to the cook." And so saying, he took off his vestments.

The Tsar had to laugh, in spite of himself. He rewarded the cook and made him Prior.

HOW THE PEASANT KEPT HOUSE

PEASANT and his wife quarreled about whose work was the hardest.

"Mine is!" said the peasant.

"No, mine is!" said his wife.

So they made a bet. The wife put on her coat, went out and did all the man's work, and then set off for town to do some shopping.

But for her husband, nothing went right. While he was carrying water, a hog upset the trough. Instead of putting vegetable oil on the potatoes, he poured on kerosene. And while he was fussing with the cow, his baby son let all the beer out of the keg.

Worst of all, though, was what happened with the cow. Instead of putting the cow out to pasture, the peasant thought he would save time by putting her up on the roof of the shed, where lots of thick grass had grown. So he got a heavy plank, put a rope around the cow's neck, and dragged her up to the roof.

But he wanted to make sure he would know if the cow should come down from the roof. So he let the free end of the rope dangle down through the chimney. Then, once he was back inside the hut, he tied the rope around his waist and started to make cabbage soup.

But the cow slid off the roof and hung on one end of the rope, meantime pulling the peasant up halfway into the chimney. And there the fellow hung, kicking his legs in the empty air.

As good luck would have it, his wife came home from town early. Seeing the cow hanging there about to expire, she ran over and cut the rope with her pocketknife. The cow fell down to the ground, and the peasant fell from the chimney straight into the cabbage soup.

"Well," his wife said to him, laughing for all she was worth, "are you going to argue with me again? Running a house is not quite so easy as falling off a log—or, for that matter, into a kettle of soup!"

So the peasant lost the bet to his wife, and he never again quarreled with her.

HOW THE PEASANT DIVIDED THE GEESE

HERE WAS once a poor peasant who had many children but no property except for one goose. He kept the goose for a long time; but the day came when there was nothing left in the house to eat, and an empty belly has no conscience. So he killed the goose, roasted it, and put it on the table.

Everything would have been fine, except there was no bread or salt. "How can we eat a meal without bread or salt?" the peasant asked his wife. "I'd better take the goose to the barin as a present, and ask him for some bread."

"Well, go ahead," said she.

So the peasant went to the barin. "Your Lordship," he said, "I have brought you this goose as a present. You are welcome to all I have. Do not refuse my humble gift, dear Master."

"Thank you, Peasant! Thank you! Now divide the goose among us without being unfair to anyone."

The barin had a wife, two sons, and two daughters, making six in all. The peasant was handed a knife, and he began to carve the goose and divide it.

He cut off the head and gave it to the barin. "You are the head of the family," he said, "so the head should go to you."

He cut off the rear end and gave it to the barin's wife. "Your job is to sit at home and look after the house, so here is the rear end for you."

He cut off the legs and gave them to the sons. "Here is a leg apiece for you, to trample your father's footpaths with."

To each of the daughters he gave a wing. "You won't live at home with your mother and father for long. When you grow up, you'll fly away," he said. "As for me, I'm just a stupid peasant at best, so I'll take the wishbone and the rest."

So the peasant got most of the goose for himself. The barin laughed, gave him some wine to drink, rewarded him with bread, and sent him home.

A prosperous peasant heard what had happened, and became envious of the poor one. He roasted five geese and took them to the barin.

"What do you want, Peasant?" asked the barin.

"Why, I've brought Your Lordship five geese as a gift."

"Thank you, my fine fellow! Now then, divide them among us without being unfair to anyone."

The peasant puzzled and pondered, but he couldn't think how to divide them equally. He just stood there scratching the back of his head.

So the barin sent for the poor peasant and told him to do the dividing.

The poor peasant took one goose and gave it to the barin and his wife, saying, "That makes three of you."

He gave another goose to the two sons, and another to the two daughters. "That makes three of you and three of you."

The last two geese he took for himself. "And that makes three of us," said he.

"Well done! Very well done!" said the barin. "You managed to divide things equally, and you took care of yourself besides."

Then he rewarded the poor peasant with money and threw the rich one out of the house.

THE MISER

HERE ONCE LIVED a wealthy merchant named Mark who was as stingy as stingy could be. One day he went out for a walk. As he was going along the road he saw a beggar. The old man was sitting by the roadside asking for alms, saying, "Good Christians, give me a little something for the sake of Christ!"

Mark the Wealthy went right on by. But a poor peasant who was coming along behind him took pity on the beggar and gave him a kopeck.

Mark the Wealthy felt ashamed of himself. So he stopped and said to the peasant, "Fellow countryman, will you lend me a kopeck? I want to give something to the beggar, but I don't have any small change."

The peasant gave him the kopeck and asked, "When should I come to get what you owe me?"

"Come tomorrow."

The next day the poor peasant went to see the rich man. He entered the broad courtyard and inquired, "Is Mark the Wealthy at home?"

"I'm here," Mark the Wealthy called out from inside the house. "What do you want?"

"I came to collect my kopeck."

"How sad! I don't happen to have any small change right now. Come back some other time."

"I'll come back tomorrow."

When he returned the next morning, he heard the same story. "I don't have any small coins on me. Can you give me change for this hundred-ruble bill? If not, come back in two weeks."

Two weeks later the poor man came back. Mark the Wealthy saw him through the window and said to his wife, "Listen carefully, Wife. I'm going to take off all my clothes and lie down under the ikons. You cover me with a shroud and then sit down and weep over me as if I were dead. When the peasant asks for his kopeck, tell him I died today."

The wife did what her husband had told her to do and sat there weeping many a bitter tear. When the peasant came into the room, she asked, "What do you want?"

"I came to collect my kopeck from Mark the Wealthy," said he.

"Ach, Peasant, my poor husband passed away just now! But before he did, he wished you a long life."

"May he enter the Kingdom of Heaven! Allow me, ma'am, to perform a small service for my kopeck. The least I can do is wash his sinful body." With these words, he snatched up a kettle of boiling water and threw it on Mark the Wealthy. Mark could hardly bear it. He winced with pain, and his feet jerked.

"Jerk and kick away—you're still going to pay!" said the peasant.

He washed the body and dressed it for burial. "Now, ma'am," he said, "go out and buy a coffin, and then have him taken to the church. I'll read the psalter over him."

Mark the Wealthy was put in his coffin and carried to the church, where the peasant started reading the psalter over him.

It grew late and very dark. Suddenly a window was opened, and a gang of thieves broke into the church. The peasant hid behind the altar.

When the thieves had gathered all their loot, they began to divide it among themselves. They divvied up everything until all that was left was a golden sword. Each one of them grabbed hold of it and tugged, refusing to let any of the others have it.

The peasant jumped out from behind the altar and shouted, "Why are you quarreling? The one who cuts off the dead man's head can have the sword!"

At this, Mark the Wealthy, scared out of his wits, sat straight up in the coffin. The thieves, who were scared even worse, took to their heels, leaving their loot behind them.

"Well, Peasant," said Mark the Wealthy, "let's divide the money."

They split it between the two of them, and each one got a lot.

"Now, then," said the poor peasant, "what about my kopeck?"

"Eh, my friend! As you yourself can see, I don't have any small change."

So Mark the Wealthy never did pay back the kopeck.

THE FOX AND THE WOLF*

NE DAY an old man said to his old wife: "Old wife, bake me a pie. And while you're baking it, I'll go out and catch us some fish."

The old man caught a whole cartload of fish. On the way back home, he saw a fox lying in the road, all curled up like a pretzel.

He got down from the cart and went up to the fox. But the animal didn't budge: he just lay as though he was dead.

"What luck!" the old man said to himself. "Now old wife will have a collar for her coat."

He put the fox in the cart and drove on toward home.

But the fox, who wasn't really dead at all, took advantage of the opportunity and began to throw the fishes out of the cart, one by one.

When he had thrown all the fishes out of the cart, he himself climbed off—very quietly.

When the old man got home he called to his old wife: "Old wife, come and see the fine collar I've brought home for your coat!"

* A folk tale retold by A. N. Tolstoy.

The old woman came out of the house. But when she went up to the cart and looked, there was nothing in it: no fur collar, no fishes, nothing.

She began to rail at the old man. "You old windbag! Always making promises and never keeping them!"

Then the old man realized that the fox had not really been dead at all. He wept and he groaned, but there was nothing he could do.

Meantime the fox had gone back along the road, picking up all the fishes as he went. He piled all of them into a heap and began to eat.

A wolf came along. "Hello, friend," he said. "May I be your guest?"

"I'm eating what belongs to me. Just keep your distance, if you please."

"Give me some of your fish?"

"Catch them yourself. Then you can have some."

"I don't know how."

"You don't? But *I* caught *mine*. It's easy. All you have to do, friend, is go to the river and stick your tail down through the ice hole. Then you just sit there and call to the fishes:

Little fish, big fish, come and catch hold!
Little fish, big fish, come and catch hold!

"If you do that, the fishes will come all by themselves and grab hold of your tail. And the longer you sit there, the more fishes you'll catch."

The wolf went to the river, stuck his tail down through the ice hole, sat there, and called out:

Little fish, big fish, come and catch hold!
Little fish, big fish, come and catch hold!

But the fox crept up near the wolf, and kept saying over and over:

> *The stars shine bright in the heavens above.*
> *Freeze, freeze, O tail of the wolf!*

The wolf asked the fox: "What is that you keep saying, my friend?"

And the fox said, "I'm helping you. I'm telling the fishes to come and grab hold of your tail." And he called out again:

> *The stars shine bright in the heavens above.*
> *Freeze, freeze, O tail of the wolf!*

The wolf sat all night with his tail in the ice hole. When morning was near, he tried to get up, but he couldn't. He thought to himself: "Aha! I've caught so many fishes I can't get up!"

Just then the old woman came along with a bucket to get some water. When she saw the wolf she cried out: "A wolf! A wolf! Chase him! Catch him!"

The wolf tugged with all his might, but he could not get his tail out of the ice hole. The old woman dropped her bucket, grabbed a heavy piece of wood, and began to beat the wolf. She beat him and beat him. The wolf struggled and struggled. Finally he broke off his tail and took to his heels. "All right for you, my friend!" he thought, as he ran away. "I'll get even with you!"

But the fox, meanwhile, had sneaked into the old woman's hut. He found some bread dough in a bowl, ate as much as he wanted, and smeared the rest of it over his face. Then he went out and lay on the road, moaning with pain.

The wolf came along. "So," said he, "that's the way you teach a friend to catch fish! Just look at me! They gave me a terrible beating!"

Said the fox, "Eh, my friend! You may have lost your tail, but your head is still in one piece. Just look at me, though! They knocked my brains out!"

"So they did," said the wolf. "Just tell me, friend, where it is you want to go, and I'll carry you on my back."

The fox got up on the wolf's back, and off they went.

As they trotted along, the fox sang very quietly:

> *The beaten one carries the one who's untouched.*
> *The beaten one carries the one who's untouched.*

The wolf asked, "What's that you keep repeating, my friend?"
"Oh, that?" said the fox. "Why, I'm just singing:

> *The beaten one carries another such.*
> *The beaten one carries another such.*"

"Right you are," said the wolf.

THE BUBBLE, THE STRAW, AND THE SHOE

BUBBLE, a Straw, and a Shoe set out one day to cut wood in the forest. They came to a river and did not know how to get across.

The Shoe said to the Bubble, "I'll tell you what let's do. The two of us will get on you and just float across."

"No, Shoe, I have a better idea. If the Straw stretches out from one bank to the other, we can cross over on it."

The Straw stretched itself out. The Shoe started across, but the Straw broke. The Shoe fell into the water, and the Bubble laughed and laughed until it burst.

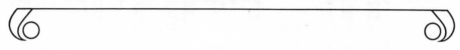

N A CERTAIN KINGDOM, in a certain land, there once lived an old man and old woman with a son named Martin. All his life the old man had been a hunter, catching and killing wild beasts and fowl by way of feeding himself and his family. When his time came, the old man fell ill and died. Martin and his mother mourned and wept for a week, but to no avail: the dead can't be brought back to life. By the end of the week they found themselves with nothing more in the house to eat.

Now the old man had left them two hundred rubles. Martin's mother was loath to pry open the money box, but what could she do? It was either spend the money or starve to death. So she counted out a hundred rubles and gave them to Martin, saying, "Here, my son. Go borrow a horse from the neighbor and then go into town and buy us some food. Perhaps we can get through the winter somehow, and then in the spring we can look for work."

Martin borrowed a horse and cart from the neighbor and went into town. As he passed by the butcher shop, he saw a crowd of people outside it, and heard some men shouting and swearing. He stopped to see what was going on.

92

The butchers had tied a hound to a post and were beating it with big, heavy sticks. The dog, yelping and snapping at them, was struggling to break loose.

Martin ran up to the butchers. "Stop it, fellows!" he cried. "Why are you beating that dog so cruelly?"

"Because he deserves it," one of them answered. "He ruined a whole side of beef—damn him, anyway!"

"Instead of beating him," said Martin, "why don't you sell him to me?"

"Gladly," said the butcher, making a joke of it. "But he'll cost you a hundred rubles."

Martin took out the money his mother had given him. "Here," he said, handing it to the butcher. Then he untied the dog, and walked off. The dog followed him, wagging his tail and rubbing against Martin's leg. He seemed to understand that Martin had saved his life.

When they reached home, Martin's mother asked him, "Well, my son, what did you buy?"

"I bought the first piece of good luck I met up with."

"What kind of nonsense is that? What piece of good luck?"

"That dog," Martin said, pointing to the hound. "I call him Zhurka the Growler."

"And that's all you bought?"

"If I'd had any money left, I probably would have bought something else besides. But he cost me the whole hundred rubles."

The old woman began to scold. "We don't have anything left to eat. Today I used the last scrapings from the bin to bake a dry-meal cake. Tomorrow we won't have even that!"

The next day she took out the last hundred rubles and gave it to Martin, saying, "Take this, my son. Go into town and buy us some food. But don't throw the money away on nothing."

Martin went into town and was walking through the streets,

looking around, when he saw a bad boy dragging a cat behind him by means of a rope looped around the cat's neck.

"Wait!" cried Martin. "Where are you dragging that pussycat?"

"To the river to drown him—damn him, anyway!"

"What did he do that was wrong?"

"He stole a pie from the table."

"Don't drown him. Sell him to me instead."

"All right. Give me a hundred rubles for him."

Martin didn't spend much time thinking it over. He took out the money, paid the boy, put the cat in a bag, and went back home.

"What did you buy, son?" his old mother asked him.

"I bought Vaska the cat."

"And you didn't buy anything else?"

"If I'd had any money left over, I probably would have bought something else."

"Ach, what a simpleton!" his old mother cried. "Get out of this house! Go and seek your bread among strangers!"

Martin set out for the neighboring village to look for work, with Zhurka and Vaska trotting along behind him. On the way he met up with the parish priest.

"Where are you going, my son?" asked the priest.

"I'm going to hire out as a farm hand."

"Come to work for me. It's true that I give no contract. But the man who works for me for a full three years will not be disappointed."

Martin accepted. For three summers and three winters he worked tirelessly for the parish priest. When the time came for him to be paid, his master called to him and said, "Now, Martin, come along with me and get your wages."

He led Martin to his storehouse and showed him two bulging bags. "Take your choice," said he.

Martin looked. One of the bags was full of silver, and the other was full of sand. "There is more to this than meets the eye," Martin said to himself. "Maybe all my hard work will come to naught, but I'm still going to take a chance. I'll choose the sand and see what happens." So he said, "Father, I'll take the bag full of fine sand."

"Well, my son," said the priest, "your choice is your own. If you scorn the silver, then take the sand."

Martin hoisted the bag of sand up on his back and set out to look for another job. He walked and he walked until he found himself in a deep, dark forest. In the forest there was a clearing, and in the clearing there was a fire, and in the fire sat a maiden of such great beauty that it couldn't be dreamed of or guessed at, but only told in a tale.

The beautiful maiden cried out to him, "Martin the Widow's Son! If you want to find happiness, save me! Take the sand for which you worked three full years and douse these flames with it!"

"To be sure," thought Martin, "it is better to help a human being than to keep on lugging this heavy load. And sand is of no great value: you can find lots of it anywhere."

So he put down the bag, untied it, and spread the sand on the flames. They were extinguished at once. At the same time, the beautiful maiden struck the ground, turned into a snake, leaped up on the goodly youth, and wound herself around his neck. Martin was terror-struck.

"Fear not!" the snake said to him. "Go now to the thrice-ninth land, to the thrice-tenth empire, and down into the underground kingdom, where my father holds sway. When you come to his palace, he will offer you much gold, much silver, and many precious stones. Accept none of these things, however. Instead, ask him for the ring on his little finger. It is no ordinary ring. If you toss it from one hand to the other, a dozen stalwart young men will appear. And whatever you order them to do, it will be accomplished in the space of one night."

So Martin, that goodly youth, set off on his journey. Whether he went a long way or a short one, whether quickly or not, he came to the thrice-tenth empire, and there he saw a huge rock. A snake slid down from the rock, struck the earth, and was transformed into the beautiful maiden he had seen before.

"Follow me!" said the beautiful maiden, and she led the way down under that same rock.

When they had gone for a long time through the underground passage, light suddenly broke upon them. It became lighter and lighter, and then they came out upon a broad field under a clear sky. In that field stood a magnificent palace, and in that palace dwelt the beautiful maiden's father—the sovereign of the underground kingdom.

The travelers entered the palace of white stone and were greeted with much affection by the King.

"Welcome, my darling daughter!" said he. "Where have you hidden yourself all this time?"

"Dearest Father mine!" she replied. "I should have perished utterly, had it not been for this young man here. He saved me from an evil, inevitable death and brought me back home."

"My thanks to you, goodly youth!" said the King. "You must needs be rewarded for your good deed. Take as much as you want of gold or silver or precious stones."

But Martin the Widow's Son replied, "May it please Your Majesty, I need neither gold nor silver nor precious stones. If you wish to reward me, give me the ring from Your Majesty's hand—the ring on the little finger. You see, I am an unmarried man. I would look at the ring from time to time, lost in thoughts of my bride-to-be, and that way I'd dispel all my loneliness."

The King at once took off the ring and gave it to Martin. "Here, keep it for good luck," said he. "But make sure you tell no one about it. Otherwise you'll get into great trouble!"

Martin the Widow's Son thanked the King, accepted the ring and a small sum of money for his return trip, and went back along the same road by which he had come. Whether he went a long way or a short one, whether quickly or not, he returned to his homeland, sought out his old mother, and they dwelt together and prospered without any hardships or sorrow.

The time came when Martin wanted to take a wife. He kept after his mother to go and get him a bride. "Go to the King himself," said he, "and ask for the hand of the beautiful Princess."

"Eh, my son!" his old mother replied. "What are you thinking of? 'Twere better for you to woo someone more like yourself. Why should I go to see the King? We know what would happen. He would get angry and have the both of us killed."

"Have no fear, Mother mine," said Martin. "If I tell you to go, then surely you can go ahead boldly. Whatever answer the King may make, you can tell me about it. But if there is no answer to bring me, then don't come back!"

So the old woman made ready and hobbled off to the King's palace. She went through the courtyard and right up the front staircase without even having been announced.

But the guards seized her. "Halt, you old hag!" they commanded. "Just where do you think you're going? Not even generals make bold to enter here without having been announced!"

"You idiots!" the old woman shouted. "I came here for a good purpose—to arrange a marriage between the King's daughter and my son. What do you mean, seizing me by the skirts?" And she set up a frightful din.

Hearing her shrieks, the King looked out of the window and commanded that she be brought into his presence.

She entered and made a low bow.

"What is your business, old woman?" the King inquired.

"Well, Your Majesty, here I am," said she. "Please excuse the expression, Sire, but I have a merchant and you have some merchandise. The merchant is my son Martin—a most clever lad indeed. And the merchandise is your daughter, the beautiful Princess. Will you give her in marriage to my Martin? They would make quite a pair, I must say!"

"What's the matter with you?" the King shouted. "Have you gone out of your mind?"

"By no means, Your Majesty. Would you deign to give me an answer?"

Within the hour, the King assembled his counselors, and they began to deliberate as to what kind of answer to give the old woman. And the result of their deliberations was this: That within the space of one night, Martin should build a splendid palace; that from this palace a crystal bridge should be built, reaching to the King's palace; that along both sides of the bridge, trees bearing golden and silver apples should grow; and that various birds should sit and sing in those trees. Furthermore, that Martin should cause to be built a five-domed cathedral. If Martin could accomplish these things, he would win the hand of the Princess, and they would be wed in the five-domed cathedral. If not, both he and his old mother would lose their heads.

Having given the old woman this answer, they sent her home.

Off she went, hobbling along and weeping many a bitter tear. When she got home she said to her son, "Well, I told you not to bite off more than you could chew. Now we'll both lose our poor, stupid heads!" And she told him what the King's answer had been.

"Cease your weeping, Old Mother!" said Martin. "We may

not lose our heads after all. Just go to bed and get a good sleep. The morning is wiser than the evening."

At the stroke of midnight, Martin got up from his bed, went out into the yard, and tossed his magic ring from one hand to the other. At once twelve stalwart young men appeared before him, alike in face, figure, and voice. "What can we do for you, Martin the Widow's Son?" they asked.

"Here is what you can do for me. Right here on this spot, build me a splendid palace, with a crystal bridge spanning the space between it and the palace of the King. Along both sides of that bridge, there should be trees bearing golden and silver apples, and various birds should sit in the branches and sing. Also, you must build me a five-domed cathedral where the Princess and I can be wed. All this must be done by first light tomorrow."

The twelve stalwart young men replied, "By morning it will be done!" Then they rushed off in different directions and came back in a moment with carpenters, masons, and other workmen. They all set about their tasks, working with wondrous swiftness.

When Martin awoke the next morning he found himself in a handsome, high-ceilinged bed chamber with elegant furnishings: he was in his own palace! When he went out on the balcony, he saw that everything else was there too: the cathedral, the crystal bridge, and the trees with the golden and silver apples.

At this same time, the King stepped out on his own balcony and peered through his spyglass. He couldn't believe what he saw! Everything he had commanded had been accomplished!

He sent for his daughter, the beautiful Princess, and said to her, "Little did I think or imagine that I would ever give thee in marriage to the son of a peasant! But now it cannot be avoided."

The Princess went to bathe and put on her costly robes for the wedding. Martin, meantime, stepped out into his broad courtyard and tossed his magic ring from one hand to the other. At once the twelve stalwart young men appeared and asked, "What are your wishes?"

"Provide me," said Martin, "with the rich raiment of a nobleman. And see that I have a coach, finely ornamented and drawn by six handsome horses."

"It will be done at once!" said they. And in less than the twinkling of an eye, they brought him an elegant cloak. He tried it on, and it fitted him perfectly. Then he turned around, and there in the courtyard stood a fine carriage drawn by six horses with coats of silver and gold.

Martin got into the coach and drove off to the cathedral. The church bells had already rung for Mass, and a great many people had assembled. Soon after Martin's arrival the Princess came in with her nursemaids and her attendants; and after her came the King and all of his ministers. When Mass had been sung, Martin took the hand of the beautiful Princess, and there and then they were wed.

The King gave his new son-in-law a big dowry and high rank, and held a great wedding feast to which everyone came. Then Martin and the Princess began their new life together.

Hardly a day passed but what Martin made use of his magic ring to embellish his palace grounds with new buildings, parks, and gardens. But none of this made the Princess happy. She just sulked and sulked because she had been married to a peasant's son instead of a Prince. And she began to look for a way to get rid of him.

The main thing, she knew, was to find out the secret of Martin's magical powers. So she started to fawn upon him and pamper him in every way you can imagine, all the while trying to get him to tell her his secret. But Martin held firm and told her nothing.

But finally she got her chance. One evening during a banquet at the King's palace, Martin drank more wine than he should have. When he came home and lay down to rest, the Princess began to kiss and caress him. She coaxed and coaxed, until finally he told her about the magic ring, and how it worked wonders.

"Now," thought the Princess, "I'll settle the score!"

As soon as Martin was sound asleep, she took the ring from his little finger, went out to the courtyard, and tossed the ring from one hand to the other. In a flash, the twelve stalwart young men appeared. "What are your wishes, beautiful Princess?" they asked.

"By tomorrow morning," said she, "all these things—the palace, the bridge, and the cathedral—must be gone. In their place let the old hut reappear. Let my husband be poor once again. And as for me, I command you to carry me away to the thrice-ninth land, to the thrice-tenth empire, to the Mouse Kingdom. For me to live here is so shameful I cannot bear it!"

"All this will be done!" said they. And that same moment, the wind wafted her away to the thrice-tenth empire, to the Mouse Kingdom.

The next morning, when the King awoke, he went out on his balcony and peered through his spyglass. But the palace with the crystal bridge and the cathedral with the five domes—all this had vanished. In its place stood only an old, broken-down hut.

"What can this mean?" the King wondered. "Where has everything gone?" And without further delay, he sent one of his adjutants to find out what had happened.

The adjutant mounted his horse and galloped off. When he came back, he reported, "Your Majesty, where the splendid palace once was, there is now only an old, wretched hut. Your son-in-law lives there in poverty with his old mother. As for your daughter, the beautiful Princess, there is no trace of her. No one knows where she is."

The King was enraged. He called a great council to pass judgment on his son-in-law for having entranced the Princess and caused her to perish. Martin was sentenced as follows: to be imprisoned in a great tower of white stone, with nothing to eat or drink, until he should die.

Stonemasons were called, and they built the high tower. There Martin was put, completely cut off from the world except for one tiny window to let in a bit of light.

One day went by, then a second, and a third. Poor Martin, locked up in the tower, had neither food nor drink. He wept piteously.

His dog Zhurka learned of his misfortune, and ran to the old hut, where he found Vaska the cat lying on the brick stove, purring contentedly.

"What a lowlife you are!" he told Vaska. "All you know how to do is lie on the stove and stretch yourself! Haven't you heard that our master is locked up in the tower? It's plain to see that you have forgotten his kindness toward you—the time when he paid a hundred rubles for you and saved your life. But for him, the worms would have eaten you long ago! Get up this minute! We must do all we can to help him!"

Vaska jumped down from the stove and went off with Zhurka. When they got to the tower, Vaska climbed up and crawled in through the little window. "Hey, Master!" he said. "Are you still alive?"

"Just barely," Martin replied. "I'm all wasted away from hunger. It's for sure that I'll starve to death."

"Just be patient and don't despair!" said Vaska. "We'll see that you get both food and drink." Then he crawled back through the window and climbed down to the ground.

"Well, Zhurka,'" he said, "our master is dying of hunger, no doubt about that. Can we think up some trick to help him?"

"Vaska, you're such a simpleton! You can't even think up a trick like that! Here's what we'll do. We'll go into town, and as soon as we meet up with a baker's boy carrying a tray on his head, I'll get under his feet and trip him. He'll let the tray fall from his head. Then you can snatch up the rolls and the bread and take them to our master. But just make sure you don't fail!"

So they went into town and walked down the main street. Soon they met up with a baker's apprentice. Zhurka got under his feet, and he stumbled, spilling his trayful of bread and rolls. Then, thinking that such a dog must surely be mad, he took to his heels in terror.

Vaska snatched up one roll and ran off with it to his master. Then he came back for another and still another.

This task accomplished, Zhurka and Vaska bethought themselves of going to the thrice-tenth empire, to the Mouse Kingdom, to bring back the magic ring. So, when they had brought Martin enough supplies to last for a year—since they knew their trip would be a long one—they said, "Master, eat and drink what you want. But remember: these supplies must last you until we return." And then they set off.

They went maybe a long way, maybe a short one, traveling either fast or not, and came to the big blue sea. Said Zhurka to Vaska, "I think I can swim to the other side. What about you?"

"I'm not much good at swimming. I'd drown right away."

"Well, climb up on my back, then."

So Vaska the cat climbed up on the back of Zhurka the dog. He dug his claws into Zhurka's coat so he wouldn't slip off, and they swam out to sea.

They swam clear across and came to the thrice-tenth empire, to the Mouse Kingdom.

In that kingdom there was not a single human being to be seen. On the other hand, there were so many mice that you couldn't count them all. Wherever you looked there were herds of mice!

Said Zhurka to Vaska, "Old buddy, it's time we went hunting! You start killing these mice, and I'll gather them up and pile them in heaps."

Vaska was used to this kind of hunting. He went after the mice in his own way, and each time he pounced, another mouse was done for. Zhurka could hardly keep up with him, as he stacked up the dead mice. And by the end of one week he had built a huge pile of them.

A great sorrow descended upon the Mouse Kingdom. The Mouse King noticed that the ranks of his tribe were thinning—that many of his subjects were doomed to death. So he crawled out of his hole and came to beg mercy from Zhurka and Vaska.

"O mighty warriors!" said he. "I bow low before you! Have mercy on my poor little tribe! Please don't destroy us entirely! Instead, tell me what service I may render you."

Then Zhurka said, "In your kingdom there is a palace, and in that palace lives a beautiful Princess. She stole a magic ring from our master. Either you get that ring for us, or you yourself will perish, together with your whole kingdom. All will be devastated."

"Hold off," said the Mouse King. "I'll assemble my subjects and ask them."

Then he summoned all the mice, both large and small, and asked them: "Is there not one among you who will make bold to go into the palace and get the magic ring?"

A tiny mouse spoke up. "I have often been in the palace," said he, "and I can tell you this: in the daytime the Princess wears the ring on her little finger, but at night, when she goes to bed, she puts it in her mouth."

"Very well," said the Mouse King, "try to get the ring. If you succeed, you'll receive a King's reward."

The tiny mouse waited until nightfall. Then he went into the palace and quietly crept into the boudoir of the Princess. She was sound asleep. He climbed up on the bed, stuck his tail into her nose, and began to tickle her nostrils. She sneezed, and the ring flew out of her mouth and fell on the rug.

The tiny mouse jumped down from the bed, snatched up the ring, and ran off with it to his King.

The Mouse King gave the ring to those two mighty warriors, Vaska the cat and Zhurka the dog, and they thanked him. Then the question arose as to who should have the safekeeping of the ring.

"Give it to me," said Vaska. "I wouldn't lose it for anything in the world!"

"All right," said Zhurka. "But be sure to guard it with your life!"

The cat put the ring in his mouth, and they set out on the homeward trek.

At length they came to the big, blue sea. Vaska jumped up on Zhurka's back and held on with his claws as tightly as he could, as Zhurka went into the water and started to swim across the sea.

Zhurka swam for one hour, and then another. Suddenly, from out of nowhere, a crow came flying. He settled on Vaska's back and started to peck at his head. What could the poor cat do? If he let loose his hold so as to use his claws on the crow, he would very likely fall into the sea and drown. If he used his teeth on his enemy, he would risk losing the ring from his mouth. It was a bad situation, either way!

Vaska held out for a long time, but finally he could stand it no longer—the crow was pecking so hard at his heroic head that it started to bleed. He got into a rage and went for the crow with his teeth, scaring him off. But meanwhile the ring fell out of his mouth and into the sea.

When they reached the other side of the sea, Zhurka at once asked about the ring. But Vaska just stood there, hanging his head. "Forgive me, old friend, for the wrong I have done. I let it fall into the sea."

"What a stupid one you are!" cried Zhurka. "You're lucky I didn't know sooner, or I'd have dumped you into the sea as well —you and your gaping mouth! Now what can we bring to our master? Get back in the water and find that ring; if you don't, it's all up with you!"

"What good would it do if I lost my life? We'd do better to think up something clever. Remember how we went hunting for mice? This time, let's go hunting for crabs."

Zhurka agreed, and they set off along the seashore, killing crabs and piling them up in stacks. Soon they had a huge heap of them.

Then a great big crab came out of the water and crawled edge-wise along the shore in search of fresh air. Zhurka and Vaska jumped on him and began to torment him.

"O mighty warriors!" cried the crab. "Please don't do me to death! I am King of all crabs; and whatever you order, I will do."

"We dropped a ring in the ocean," said Zhurka. "If you desire mercy, go find it and bring it to us. Otherwise, we'll lay waste your whole kingdom!"

Without further delay, King Crab summoned all of his subjects and began to question them about the ring. A very small crab spoke up. "I know where the ring is," he said. "As it was falling down toward the bottom of the sea, a white sturgeon saw it and gobbled it up. I was there, and I saw him."

Immediately all of the crabs plunged into the sea to look for the white sturgeon. When they found the poor fish, they began to torment him with their pincers. They kept after him and didn't give him a minute's rest. He swam this way and that, around and around, and ended up on the seashore.

The King of the Crabs crawled out of the water and bowed to Zhurka and Vaska. "O mighty warriors," said he, "here is the white sturgeon! Show him no mercy, for it was he who swallowed the ring!"

Zhurka pounced on the sturgeon and tore at him with his teeth, starting with the tail end. "Now," he thought, "I'll get my fill to eat!"

But Vaska, the rascal, knew where the ring was more likely to be found. He went for the sturgeon's stomach, ripped it open, and there was the ring! He snatched it up with his teeth and ran off as fast as his legs could carry him, thinking, "I'll run to our master, give him the ring, and brag that I did the whole thing myself. He'll love me for that and treat me much better than Zhurka!"

Meanwhile, Zhurka ate his fill, and then looked around. "Where is Vaska?" he wondered. But it didn't take him long to surmise what Vaska was up to.

"All right for you, you swindler!" he growled. "I'll catch up with you and tear you into shreds!"

So he took out after him. He chased Vaska for maybe a long time, maybe a short one, and caught up with him, threatening him with a disaster he could not escape. But Vaska, catching sight of a birch tree, went scampering up it and sat there on the very top branch.

"Have it your own way," said Zhurka. "You can't sit up there for the rest of your life. Sooner or later, you'll have to climb down. Meantime I won't stir one step from this spot!"

For three whole days, Vaska sat up there in the top of the birch tree; and for three whole days, Zhurka kept a close watch on him. Finally both of them got hungry, so they agreed on an armistice.

Having made peace, they set out on the homeward trek together. When they got to the white stone tower, Vaska climbed up and poked his head through the little window. "Are you still alive, Master?" he asked.

"Hello there, Vaska!" said Martin. "I thought you'd never come back! I've had nothing to eat for three days."

Vaska, by way of reply, let fall the magic ring.

Martin waited until the dark of night. Then he tossed the ring from one hand to the other. At once the twelve stalwart young men appeared. "What are your wishes?" they asked.

"Bring me back my palace, brave lads," said he, "and the crystal bridge, and the five-domed cathedral. Also, bring me back my unfaithful wife. And see that you do it by tomorrow morning!"

No sooner said than done. The next morning, when the King awoke, he went out on his balcony and peered through his spyglass. Where the old hut had been, there was now a great palace. From that palace to the King's own, a crystal bridge had been built, and along both sides of the bridge were trees with golden and silver apples.

The King ordered his carriage to be brought and drove off to find out for himself whether all was indeed as it once had been, or whether it was just a vision.

Martin met him at the gateway and told him all that had happened. "And that," he concluded, "is the way the Princess dealt with me."

The King decreed the death penalty. Martin's unfaithful wife was tied to the tail of a wild stallion, and the stallion was loosed in the open fields. He flew like an arrow, smashing her body to bits against the rocks and steep gullies. But Martin still lives and thrives.

BLABBERMOUTH: Nechaev, A., *Russkie narodnye skazki. V pereskazakh A. Nechaeva,* Moscow, 1953. Hereinafter cited as "Nechaev."

THE BUBBLE, THE STRAW, AND THE SHOE: Afanas'ev, A. N., *Narodnye russkie skazki,* Moscow, 1957. Hereinafter cited as "Afanas'ev."

THE CRANE AND THE HERON: Afanas'ev.

THE FALCON UNDER THE HAT: Afanas'ev.

THE FOX AND THE WOLF: Tolstoy, A. N., *Russkie narodnye skazki, Sobranie sochineniy v desyati tomakh, t. 8,* Moscow, 1947. Also, Kapitsa, O., *Russkie skazki pro zverey,* Moscow, 1947.

HOW THE PEASANT DIVIDED THE GEESE: Afanas'ev.

HOW THE PEASANT KEPT HOUSE: Russkaya satiricheskaya skazka, Moscow, 1958.

IVAN THE MERCHANT'S SON AND VASILISA THE WISE: Afanas'ev.

THE MAGIC RING: Afanas'ev.

THE MISER: Afanas'ev.

THE MONASTERY OF NO CARES: Smirnov, A. M., *Sbornik velikorusskikh skazok arkhiva Russkogo Geograficheskogo Obshchestva,* Petrograd, 1917.

SHEMYAKA THE JUDGE: Afanas'ev. Also, *Russkie narodnye skazki, pod obshch. red. V. I. Chicherova,* Moscow, 1956, #96.

THE SHREWISH WIFE: Nechaev.

SISTER ALIONUSHKA AND BROTHER IVANUSHKA: Tolstoy, A. N., *Polnoe sobranie sochineniy, t. 12,* Moscow, 1948.

THE SNAKE: Tolstoy, L. N., *Polnoe sobranie sochineniy, t. 21,* Moscow, 1935.

THE THIEF: Afanas'ev.

ABOUT THE TRANSLATOR

Guy Daniels was born in Gilmore City, Iowa, and attended school there and later the University of Iowa, from which he was graduated *magna cum laude*. Mr. Daniels served in the United States Navy during World War II with a tour of duty in Europe and the French West Indies. He is the translator of many books from the French and Russian, and the author of poems, essays, and a novel —*Progress, U.S.A.* Mr. Daniels translated the recent Funk & Wagnalls book for children, *The Wild Beast* by Nikolai Leskov.

ABOUT THE ARTIST

Feodor Rojankovsky was born in Mitava, Russia, and attended the Fine Art Academy in Moscow. He has been the recipient of a number of citations and awards, including the Art Directors' Club medal, a U.S. Treasury Department citation in 1946, and the Caldecott Medal in 1956. From 1919 to 1925 he was stage decorator for the Poznan Opera, and he has illustrated many children's books, textbooks, and novels.